MINDTAP ACCELERATE: COMP FOUNDATIONS

CENGAGE

Australia • Brazil • Canada • Mexico • Singapore • United Kingdom • United States

MindTap Accelerate: Comp Foundations,
First Edition

Product Team Manager: Laura Ross

Product Manager: Nancy Tran

Learning Designer: Leslie Taggart

Manager, Content Delivery: Anika Bachhuber

Content Manager: Jacqueline Czel

In House SME: Anne Alexander

Subject Matter Expert: Desmond Lewis

Manager, In-House SME: Kevin O'Brien

Executive Marketing Manager: Kina Lara

Manufacturing Planner: Fola Orekoya

Art Director: Lizz Anderson

IP Analyst: Amber Hill

Digital Delivery Lead: Nikkita Kendrick

Production Service: Lumina Datamatics, Inc.

For product information and technology assistance, contact us at
**Cengage Customer & Sales Support, 1-800-354-9706 or
support.cengage.com.**

For permission to use material from this text or product,
submit all requests online at **www.cengage.com/permissions.**

Student Edition:
ISBN: 978-0-357-10657-0

Cengage
200 Pier 4 Boulevard
Boston, MA 02210
USA

Cengage is a leading provider of customized learning solutions with employees residing in nearly 40 different countries and sales in more than 125 countries around the world. Find your local representative at **www.cengage.com.**

To learn more about Cengage platforms and services, register or access your online learning solution, or purchase materials for your course, visit **www.cengage.com.**

Printed at CLDPC, USA, 07-24

Contents

Part 3 Reference Guides 218

Discover What You Want

Imagine a man who tries to buy a plane ticket for his next vacation, with no destination in mind. He pulls out his iPad and logs in to his favorite website for trip planning. He gets a screen that prompts him for details about his destination. And he leaves all the fields blank.

"I'm not fussy," says the would-be vacationer. "I just want to get away. I'll just accept whatever the computer coughs up."

Compare this person to another traveler who books a flight to Ixtapa, Mexico, departing on Saturday, March 23, and returning Sunday, April 7—window seat, first class, and vegetarian meals.

Now, ask yourself which traveler is more likely to end up with a vacation that he'll enjoy.

The same principle applies in any area of life. Knowing where we want to go increases the probability that we will arrive at our destination. Discovering what we want makes it more likely that we'll attain it.

Okay, so the example about the traveler with no destination is far-fetched. Before you dismiss it, though, do an informal experiment: Ask three other students what they want to get out of their education. Be prepared for hemming, hawing, and vague generalities.

This is amazing, considering the stakes involved. Students routinely invest years of their lives and thousands of dollars, with only a hazy idea of their destination in life.

Now suppose that you asked someone what she wanted from her education, and you got this answer: "I plan to get a degree in journalism, with double minors in earth science and Portuguese, so I can work as a reporter covering the environment in Brazil." The details of a person's vision offer clues to his or her skills and sense of purpose.

Another clue is the presence of "stretch goals"—those that are big *and* achievable. A 40-year-old might spend years talking about his desire to be a professional athlete someday. Chances are, that's no longer achievable. However, setting a goal to lose 10 pounds by playing basketball at the gym three days a week is another matter. That's a stretch—a challenge. It's also doable.

Discovering what you want helps you succeed in higher education. Many students quit school simply because they are unsure about what they want from it. With well-defined goals in mind, you can look for connections between what you want and what you study. The more connections, the more likely you'll stay in school—and get what you want in every area of life.

Six Things You Can Do Now

People who are new to higher education get a common piece of advice: "You'll get the hang of being in school. Just give it time." However, you can often *reduce* your transition time—and your initial discomfort—with the following strategies.

1. **Plug into resources.** A supercharger increases the air supply to an internal combustion engine. The resulting difference in power can be dramatic. You can make just as powerful a difference in your education if you supercharge it by using all of the resources available to students. In this case, your "air supply" includes people, campus clubs and organizations, and school and community services.

   Of all resources, people are the most important. You can isolate yourself, study hard, and get a good education. However, doing this is not the most powerful use of your tuition money. When you establish relationships with teachers, staff members, fellow students, and potential employers, you can get a *great* education.

   Accessing resources is especially important if you are the first person in your family to enter higher education. As a first-generation student, you are having experiences that people in your family may not understand. Talk to your relatives about your activities at school. If they ask how they can help you, give specific answers. Also ask your instructors about programs for first-generation students on your campus.

2. **Meet with your academic advisor.** One person in particular—your academic advisor—can help you access resources and make the transition to higher education. Meet with this person regularly. Advisors generally know about course requirements, options for declaring majors, and the resources available at your school. Peer advisors might also be available.

3. **Show up for class.** The amount that you pay in tuition and fees makes a powerful argument for going to classes regularly. In large part, the material that you're tested on comes from events that take place in class.

   Showing up for class occurs on two levels. The most visible level is being physically present in the classroom. Even more important, though, is showing up mentally. This kind of attendance includes taking detailed notes, asking questions, and contributing to class discussions.

4. **Be willing to rethink how you learn.** Many students arrive in higher education with study skills that were honed for high school. They underestimate how long it takes to complete assignments and prepare for tests. These students get an unpleasant surprise when their grades take a hit.

   To avoid this fate, embrace new strategies for learning. Don't prepare for tests by simply memorizing isolated facts. Instead, relate facts to the big ideas in your courses. State those ideas in your own words. Give examples based on personal experience whenever possible, and explain how you would apply the ideas. The strategies presented in this text can help you do all of these things.

5. **Take the initiative in meeting new people.** Realize that most of the people in this new world of higher education are waiting to be welcomed. You can help them and help yourself at the same time. Introduce yourself to classmates and instructors. Just before or after class is a good time.

6. **Admit your feelings—whatever they are.** School can be an intimidating experience for new students. People of diverse cultures, adult learners, commuters, and people with disabilities may feel excluded. Feelings of anxiety, isolation, and homesickness are common among students.

Those emotions are common among new students, and there's nothing wrong with them. Simply admitting the truth about how you feel—to yourself and to someone else—can help you cope. And you can almost always do something constructive in the present moment, no matter how you feel.

If your feelings about the transition to higher education make it hard for you to carry out the activities of daily life—going to class, working, studying, and relating to people—then get professional help. Start with a counselor at the student health service on your campus. The mere act of seeking help can make a difference.

Do you have a minute?

Make a list of questions you want to ask your advisor and rank them by priority. When you're in the meeting, be sure to start with your most important question.

Discovery, Intention, and Action

Success is no mystery. Successful people have left clues—*many* clues, in fact. There are thousands of articles and books that give tools, tips, techniques, and strategies for success. Do an Internet search on *success* and you'll get over 300 million results.

If that sounds overwhelming, don't worry. Success is simply the process of setting and achieving goals. And the essentials of that process can be described in three words: *Discovery. Intention. Action.* They work together in phases:

- Discovery—observing your thoughts, feelings, behaviors, and current circumstances
- Intention—choosing new outcomes that you'd like to create
- Action—following through with your intentions with new behaviors

Here's how

Write Discovery Statements

The first stage is a Discovery Statement. These often begin with a prompt, such as "I discovered that …" Here is an opportunity to reflect on "where you are." Discovery Statements describe your current strengths and areas for improvement. Discovery Statements can also be descriptions of your feelings, thoughts, and behavior. Whenever you get an "aha!" moment—a flash of insight or a sudden solution to a problem—put it in a Discovery Statement. To write effective Discovery Statements, remember the following.

Record the specifics about your thoughts, feelings, and behavior. Thoughts include inner voices. We talk to ourselves constantly in our head. When internal chatter gets in the way, write down what you tell yourself. If this seems difficult at first, just start writing. The act of writing can trigger a flood of thoughts.

Thoughts also include mental pictures. These are especially powerful. Picturing yourself flunking a test is like a rehearsal to do just that. One way to take away the power of negative images is to describe them in detail.

Also notice how you feel when you function well. Use Discovery Statements to pinpoint exactly where and when you learn most effectively.

In addition, observe your emotions and actions, and record the facts. If you spent 90 minutes chatting online with a favorite cousin instead of reading your anatomy text, write about it. Include the details—when you did it, where you did it, and how it felt.

Use discomfort as a signal. When you approach a hard task, such as a difficult math problem, notice your physical sensations. These might include a churning stomach, shallow breathing, and yawning. Feeling uncomfortable, bored, or tired can be a signal that you're about to do valuable work. Stick with it. Write about it. Tell yourself you can handle the discomfort just a little bit longer. You will be rewarded with a new insight.

Suspend judgment. As you learn about yourself, be gentle. Suspend self-judgment. If you continually judge your behaviors as "bad" or "stupid," your mind will quit making discoveries rather than put up with abuse. For your own benefit, be kind to yourself.

Tell the truth. Suspending judgment helps you tell the truth about yourself. "The truth will set you free" is a saying that endures for a reason. The closer you get to the truth, the more powerful your Discovery Statements. And if you notice that you are avoiding the truth, don't blame yourself. Just tell the truth about it.

Write Intention Statements

Intention Statements can be used to alter your course. They are statements of your commitment to do a specific task or achieve a goal. Discovery Statements promote awareness, whereas Intention Statements are blueprints for action. The two processes reinforce each other.

Make intentions positive. The purpose of writing Intention Statements is to focus on what you *do* want rather than what you *don't* want. Instead of writing "I will not fall asleep while studying chemistry," write, "I intend to stay awake when studying chemistry." Also avoid the word *try*. Trying is not doing. When we hedge our bets with *try*, we can always tell ourselves, "Well, I *tried* to stay awake."

Make intentions observable. Rather than writing "I intend to work harder on my history assignments," write, "I intend to review my class notes daily and make summary sheets of my reading."

Make intentions small and achievable. Break large goals into small, specific tasks that can be accomplished quickly. Small and simple changes in behavior—when practiced consistently over time—can have large and lasting effects.

When setting your goals, anticipate self-sabotage. Be aware of what you might do, consciously or unconsciously, to undermine your best intentions. Also be careful about intentions that depend on other people. If you intend for your study group to complete an assignment by Monday, then your success depends on the students in the group. Likewise, you can support your group's success by following through on your own stated intentions.

Set time lines. For example, if you are assigned a paper to write, break the assignment into small tasks and set a precise due date for each one: "I intend to select a topic for my paper by 9 a.m. Wednesday."

Integrity...making time for what matters most

Living with integrity is a challenge. For example, people might tell you that they're open-minded—and then get angry when you disagree with them. Students might say that they value education—and then skip classes to party. When our words and actions get out of alignment, then we stop getting the results that we want.

One solution is to define your values as high-priority activities. In your journal, brainstorm ways to complete this sentence: *It's extremely important that I make time for ...* Then use your answers to set goals, schedule events, and write daily to-do lists. This strategy translates your values into plans that directly affect the way you manage time.

For example, perhaps it's important for you to stay healthy. Then you can set goals to exercise regularly and manage your weight. In turn, those goals can show up as items on your to-do list and calendar—commitments to go to the gym, take an aerobics class, and include low-fat foods on your grocery list.

The ultimate time management skill is to define your values and align your actions.

Act Now!

Carefully crafted Discovery Statements are a beauty to behold. Precise Intention Statements can inspire awe. But neither will be of much use until you put them into action. This is where the magic happens.

Life responds to what you *do*. Successful people are those who consistently produce the results that they want. And results follow from specific, consistent behaviors. If you want new results in your life, then take new actions.

Get physical. This phase of the process is about moving from thinking to doing. Translate goals into physical actions that would show up on a video recording. Get your legs, arms, and mouth moving.

Welcome discomfort. Changing your behavior might lead to feelings of discomfort. Instead of going back to your old behaviors, befriend the yucky feelings. Taking action has a way of dissolving discomfort.

When you get stuck, tell the truth about it. As you become a student of human behavior, you'll see people expecting new results from old behaviors—and then wondering why they feel stuck. Don't be surprised if you discover this tendency in yourself. Just tell the truth about it, review your intentions, and take your next action.

| **1-1** | Reading for Topics, Main Ideas, and Details |

Review

Identify the topic and main idea of an essay.

The **topic** of the essay is what the essay is about; it is the larger, broader issue that the essay focuses on. The **main idea** is the point of the essay, and it's contained in the **thesis statement,** which is often the last sentence of the first paragraph in an essay. The thesis statement includes the topic as well as a controlling idea about the topic, such as a focus, an opinion, or an argument. To tell the difference between the topic and the main idea, think of the topic as the larger issue and the main idea as the more focused, specific point about that issue.

Identify the thesis statement of an essay.

The thesis is the main idea that will be developed throughout the rest of the piece. To find the thesis statement, first, determine the topic of the essay or article. Second, look for a sentence that includes both this topic and a particular point (controlling idea) about that topic. Once you find what you believe to be the topic and thesis statement of an essay, look at its major details to check to see if you have correctly identified the thesis.

Identify the major and minor details in the body paragraphs of an essay.

Major details are the supporting ideas that directly relate to and support the main idea of the essay, while **minor details** support the major details. They can do this by explaining the major detail in more depth or by providing more information about them. Not every major detail is supported by minor details. Major and minor details appear in the body paragraphs of an essay, which follow the introduction.

Recognize types of support in an essay.

The kinds of support you will see depend on the types of essays that you're reading. For example, if you are asked to read a paragraph about an intern's first week at a company, you might see that the author uses descriptions and anecdotes, but if you are reading an essay about the effects of authoritarian governments on social policies, you would likely see reasons, explanations, facts and statistics, expert opinions, and maybe quotations from significant figures to support the thesis statement. Commonly used types of support are examples, facts and statistics, reasons, explanations, anecdotes, descriptions, steps and procedures, and quotations from experts.

| **1-1a** | Reading for Topics, Main Ideas, and Details |

In each set, identify one Topic (T), one Main Idea (MI), and one Detail (D).

1. _____ School shopping at the mall is an exhausting process for parents.

   _____ Shopping in the mall.

   _____ Buying tennis shoes is probably the most difficult task to accomplish while school shopping.

2. _____ Biology is a very popular major at many colleges.

   _____ Choosing a major.

   _____ Selecting a major is sometimes based on interest and popularity of the major in college.

3. _____ Military branches.

   _____ The United States Coast Guard is the least discussed branch of the military.

   _____ There are five branches of the United States Military: Army, Navy, Marines, Air Force and Coast Guard.

4. _____ Watching sports is Americans' favorite pastime.

   _____ Football is the most watched team sport in America.

   _____ Sports.

5. _____ Exercising for health.

   _____ Exercise is good for the heart, lungs, and muscles.

   _____ Jogging is a good way to improve lung capacity.

6. _____ More skinny jeans are sold today than any other types of pants.

   _____ Many people buy jeans, shirts and accessories throughout the year.

   _____ Clothes.

7. _____ Music on the radio.

   _____ Pop music is the most frequently played genre of music on radio.

   _____ Radio stations usually play R & B/ hip-hop, pop, or country music.

8. _____ Today, the most successful movies are action films, comedies, and documentaries.

   _____ Popular movie genres.

   _____ Documentaries have grown to become a very lucrative film genre over the years.

| **1-1b** | Reading for Topics, Main Ideas, and Details |

Directions: *Choose the best answer based on the paragraph for the questions that follow.*

Education

(1) Education in the United States is an important issue that arises each year. (2) Students who graduate from high school and attain a post-secondary education have more economic opportunities compared to their counterparts who do not graduate from high school. (3) In fact, earning potential increases significantly with attainment of credentials and degrees. (4) As society shifts to demanding more technology-based jobs, the importance of education grows due to the required skills needed for these jobs. (5) Moreover, an education provides people with job security. (6) Therefore, education in America is essential due to earning potential, changes in technology, and job security.

1. What is the topic of the paragraph? _____

2. What sentence expresses the main idea of the paragraph? _____

    _____

3. List three supporting details.

    a. _____

    b. _____

    c. _____

4. Circle the topic and underline the main idea of sentence 3:

    In fact, earning potential increases significantly with attainment of credentials and degrees.

5. Circle the topic and underline the main idea of sentence 1:

    Education in the United States is an important issue that arises each year.

    Directions: *Circle the topic of each of the following titles.*

6. "How to Spot Fake News," by Eugene Kiely and Lori Robertson

7. "Cyberbullying is Worse than Bullying," by Gideon Lasco

8. "The Ideal Female Body Type Is Getting Even Harder to Attain," by Frances Bozsik and Brooke L. Bennett

| **1-1c** | Reading for Topics, Main Idea, and Details |

Directions: *Read the paragraph below. As a group, fill in the blanks labeled* **(a.)** *with the topic, main idea, and major details of the paragraph. For* **(b),** *each group member will create an additional minor detail that would add support to each of the major details.*

Topic: _____

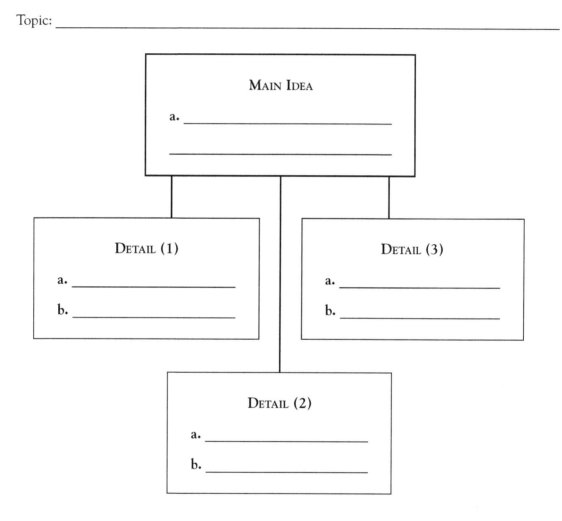

Japanese animation, known as *anime*, has become a global phenomenon. In many cases, anime is an animated version of a Japanese comic book called *Manga*. Anime's new-found growth in international popularity can be attributed to several changes over past years. First, through Internet streaming services, translated versions of anime films and television series have become easily accessible and have gained huge numbers in their audience. Next, several cable networks have contributed to the increase in the anime audience by programming scheduled blocks of anime series that have established international followings. Finally, video games based on anime series have been developed for several gaming platforms to appeal to all ages.

1-2 | Reading Critically

Review

Read actively.

First, read to understand what the writer is saying on the surface level, figure out the meaning of any unknown words, identify main ideas, and determine how they relate to one another. Connecting what the writer says to what you already know can help you understand a text.

Then think about the **context**—the circumstances surrounding the text:

- Who wrote it? Learn what you can about the author.
- Who is the author writing for, and what is important to that audience?
- Where was the text published? Was it published in a reputable source like the *Wall Street Journal* or in a supermarket tabloid like the *National Enquirer*?
- Why did the author write the piece? The author may want to inform, entertain, or persuade the audience—or may have a combination of purposes.

Distinguish between facts and opinions.

A **fact** is a piece of information that can be proven to be true. You can't disagree with a fact.

> Example of a fact: U.S. citizens can vote at age 18.

In contrast, an **opinion** is a statement of belief or judgment. You can agree or disagree with an opinion.

> Example of an opinion: An 18-year-old is too young and inexperienced to cast a considered vote.

Opinions are based on assumptions and biases. An **assumption** is an unsubstantiated or unexamined belief. A **bias** is a prejudice for or against something. Think about how the authors' assumptions and biases might affect their reasoning, and consider how your own assumptions and biases affect your reaction to what you read.

> Example of an assumption: At 18, a person is still a teenager and has no knowledge or experience of the world.

> Example of a bias: Teenagers are self-centered and immature.

Finally, notice the writer's **tone**, or how they convey emotions and attitudes toward the topic. A report on the latest cancer research may have a serious tone; a comic's blog entry might have a humorous tone. Tone is expressed through the author's word choice and writing style.

Make Inferences.

An **inference** is a conclusion you draw from the evidence the author provides. You can draw conclusions from the facts and opinions the author expresses. To read critically, however, you also need to analyze what the language, tone, and purpose imply. If a text is written in a sarcastic or ironic tone, for instance, the author probably means the opposite of the literal meaning of the words.

1-2a | Reading Critically

PART I

Directions: *Read each paragraph from an essay, which has been scrambled. Place a number from* **1–3** *next to each paragraph to indicate the correct ordering. Identify the topic and main idea of each paragraph.*

I.   ____ Fear rears its ugly head in the novel through different types of punishment. As previously mentioned, Kunte Kinte receives a swift and severe penalty for his insubordinate actions. During the time frame of *Roots*, blacks are considered chattel. Hence, they are judged under an alternative set of rules from white individuals. To maintain control over the population of slaves in the work, lynchings, beatings, rapes, non-surgical amputations and murders are often committed. These inhumane treatments achieve their desired effect, fear. Even when slaves have abandoned all hope of a worldly salvation from their torturous existence, whites enter religious realms to extend their reign of terror.

(Topic) _____ (MI)_____

II.   ____Slavery is the main means that Haley employs to display one form of fear. In the work, Africans, and those who would become African-Americans, are subjected to indignities that are unimaginable. Probably, the most memorable of these atrocities comes from a scene in the story where Kunte Kinte is force to accept his new "Christian" identity. He is asked several times to answer to the name "Toby". After refusing to acknowledge this query, half of one of his feet is chopped off. Thus, he is destined to remain a slave because he no longer possesses the ability to run. His mobility is permanently inhibited. In addition, the severing of Kinte's foot can also be applied to yet another form of fear, punishment.

(Topic) _____ (MI)_____

III.   ____Alex Haley's *Roots* expresses the concept of fear via various mediums, including indentured servitude, punishment and religion. Each of these tools of control is wielded without impunity throughout the novel. Thus, Haley presents a graphic and dynamic image of the horrific business that has become known as the peculiar institution. Moreover, the notion of fear acts the underlying theme for the entire plot, as it does for actual life.

(Topic) _____ (MI)_____

PART II

1.   What would be the best title for the selection?

_____

1-2b Reading Critically

Directions: *Use Figure 1 to answer the following questions.*

Topics, Main Ideas, and Details

Learning Objectives: Identify the topic, main idea and details.

Directions: *Choose the best answer based on the paragraph for the questions that follow.*

Education

Education in the United States is an important issue that arises each year[1]. Students who graduate from high school and attain a post-secondary education have more economic opportunities in comparison to their counterparts who do not graduate from high school[2]. In fact, earning potential increases significantly with attainment of credentials and degrees[3]. As society shifts to demanding more technology-based jobs, the importance of education grows due to the required skills needed for these jobs[4]. Moreover, an education provides people with job security[5]. Therefore, education in America is essential due to earning potential, changes in technology, and job security[6].

1. What is the topic of the paragraph?
   a. Learning
   b. Technology-based jobs
   c. Economic opportunities
   d. Education
2. What sentence expresses the main idea of the paragraph?
   a. 2
   b. 4
   c. 5
   d. 6
3. What is a supporting detail found in the paragraph?
   a. Technology-based jobs require workers to receive an education.
   b. America's population is growing.
   c. Security jobs are abundant throughout the nation.
   d. None of the above.

4. Identify the topic of sentence 3.
   a. Degrees
   b. Credentials
   c. Earning potential
   d. None of the above.
5. What is the main idea of sentence 1?
   a. America has a complex educational system.
   b. Education is an important issue in the U.S.
   c. Education.
   d. None of the above.

Directions: *Circle the topic of each of the following titles.*

6. "How to Spot Fake News", by Eugene Kiely and Lori Robertson.
7. "Cyberbullying is Worse than Bullying", by Gideon Lasco.
8. "The Ideal Female Body Type Is Getting Even Harder To Attain," by Frances Bozsik and Brooke L. Bernett.

Figure 1

1. What is the main point of the assignment?

   _____

2. Who wrote "The Ideal Female Type is Getting Even Harder to Attain"?

   _____

3. All of the following are mentioned as reason why education is important, *except*

   a. The internet

   b. Technology

   c. Job security

   d. Earning potential

4. Society demands jobs that require more what?

   _____

1-2c	Reading Critically

Directions: *Divide into groups. Choose a partner or partners within the group. Take turns reading aloud each of the following paragraphs. As each group member reads, write down the topic and main idea that you hear in your own words. Exchange and compare answers to develop a single unified topic and main idea statement for each of the paragraphs.*

I. ___ Taking English 131 online allows students to be themselves in the truest sense. When a person says, "come as you are," rarely does one mean it literally. In the case of taking an English course online, it means letting students do just that. It does matter where the person is located. He or she can access the class and the work. The life of a freshman is strenuous and ever changing. To be frank, it is fraught with lots of discomfort and formality. English 131 online can provide a student with a respite of relief from the toil and constraint of more traditional course formats. There are sure to be times that most freshmen are running late or feeling a bit sluggish. With a course that is at the ready upon demand, a new student may yet be able to hold onto a last thread of sanity during his or her first year of courses.

(Topic) _____ (MI) _____

II. ___ Sugar sweetened beverages are drinks that have add caloric sugar sweeteners. These sweeteners are not needed for any other purpose besides increase sweetness in taste. In other words, the calories created by the sweeteners are not necessary for the human body. The increased consumption, container size and availability have adversely affected a large cross section of the population of the United States. Although there are regulations in place for the distribution of said beverages, stricter laws must be instituted to immediately arrest the mounting situation.

(Topic) _____ (MI) _____

III. ___ Regarding affirmative action, I believe that it is still needed in certain circumstances. Corporate America, which includes a higher education system that is often exclusive, tends to prevent the ascension of minorities to its upper ranks. Affirmative action is one crucial safeguard that is in place to prevent the development of an even larger socio-economic gap from forming.

(Topic) _____ (MI) _____

IV. ___ Diamond admits to becoming somewhat of a "know-it-all" during family conversations. In one noted conversation, she states that her father's understanding when she openly doubted his ability to truly comprehend the gravity and complexity of the Vietnam War surprised her. After said talk, she began to define her life, as a young formative thinker, not within the confines of the safe haven of what she thought of as home, but from a more matured perspective.

(Topic) _____ (MI) _____

1-3 | Understanding Fact and Opinion

Review

Distinguish between facts and opinions.

Facts are items of information that can be proven to be true through evidence or observation. **Opinions** are personal beliefs or points of view that cannot necessarily be verified. It is important to be able to distinguish between facts and opinions as you read and to use them effectively when you write.

> Example of a **fact**: The most common type of netsuke is a carved three-dimensional figure—a sort of miniature sculpture.

> Example of an **opinion**: The most interesting netsukes are known as "trick" netsukes, which often contain delightful small sculptures tucked away within the carved exterior.

Check facts to verify the validity of an author's points.

If you have questions about a **fact** (if it does not sound right, seems unlikely, contradicts other information in an article, or does not match what you already know), mark it to follow up on later. To check facts, you can find the original source of the information to see if the author has cited it accurately, and you can use a wide variety of printed and Internet resources to get independent confirmation that the fact is true, such as encyclopedias, scholarly journals, Google Scholar, and FactCheck.org.

Use facts to support your arguments or opinions.

As a writer, you can use facts to support your points and convince your reader that your argument or point of view is well-founded or to provide additional explanations of your main ideas. Choose relevant facts and statistics from reputable sources that support your point and can be verified by your readers.

Check that opinions are accurately and sufficiently supported.

Ask yourself whether an opinion is well supported, and thus believable, or if it makes large generalizations that are not backed up with convincing evidence.

Recognize opinions disguised as facts.

Sometimes writers mask their opinions as facts, so you have to read critically.

> Example: According to a company spokesperson, employees are satisfied with the outcome of the investigation into management practices.

This sentence provides no proof that this information is correct, such as the results of an employee poll.

Use facts, statistics, anecdotes, and reasons to support opinions.

You can use facts, statistics, examples, anecdotes, and reasons as support. Be sure that you make your position clear, signal that you are expressing your opinion, and provide well-researched evidence to support your point.

1-3a | Understanding Fact and Opinion

Directions: *Identify each of the statements as a fact (F) or opinion (O). Provide an explanation for each of your answers.*

1. _____ Chocolate is the best flavor for ice cream.

2. _____ Texas has the hottest summers in America.

3. _____ Christmas is the most joyous holiday.

4. _____ Everyone loves to watch sports on Sundays.

5. _____ A human being is a homo sapiens.

6. _____ Oranges are orange.

7. _____ Albert Einstein is one of the most relevant figures in world history.

8. _____ Sundays should be days of rest and relaxation.

9. _____ In the United States, a person must be 21 years of age to drink legally.

10. _____ Drinking and driving is illegal.

11. _____ All people who commit violent crimes should be incarcerated for many years.

12. _____ Cars in the future will eventually fly.

13. _____ Cell phones are the most useful form of technology today.

14. _____ The capital of the U.S. is Washington, D.C.

15. _____ Roses are the most beautiful flowers in the world.

16. _____ Children should be prohibited from hearing music with explicit lyrics.

17. _____ Internet-based programming is going to replace cable networks by 2020.

18. _____ Next year, Sanaa Lewis will win student of the year at Foster High School.

1-3b | Understanding Fact and Opinion

Directions: *Read each of the paragraphs. Determine, based upon the information provided in the paragraph, whether the underlined portion is a fact or an opinion. In the blanks that follow, write an F (Fact) or O (Opinion), then give a brief explanation to support your answer.*

I. **(1)** I began recording the **DJ Zo Luvs Screw** CD following DJ Screw's death in November 2000. The album's concept, production, marketing and every other aspect of developing the end product was solely controlled by me. **(2)** I controlled everything because many of my employees were incompetent and lazy. Following the recording of several songs, I decided to place DJ Zo the Affiliate on the cover of the CD as a marketing tool, being that DJ Zo the Affiliate was known as DJ Screw's cousin. **(3)** I released the **DJ ZO Luvs Screw** CD in 2002. **(4)** Everybody loves DJ Zo because he is the best party DJ in Houston. Prior to its official release, I secured national distribution.

_____ 1. _____

_____ 2. _____

_____ 3. _____

_____ 4. _____

II. The High Renaissance is a period of great development of political, religious and intellectual understanding. **(1)** The period begins in the late 15th century. **(2)** The world becomes a different more diverse place to not only live, but to thrive. **(3)** Michelangelo's *Sistine Chapel* is created during this period. In exploring the many facets of the High Renaissance, one cannot help but to see a reflection of herself within the complex intricacies of High Renaissance social structure. **(4)** It is definitely a fascinating episode in human history.

_____ 1. _____

_____ 2. _____

_____ 3. _____

_____ 4. _____

<table>
<tr><td>**1-3c**</td><td>Understanding Fact and Opinion</td></tr>
</table>

Directions: *1) Have your instructor choose 5 topics or decide as a class or in groups on 5 topics. 2) Write three sentences for each topic that are either facts or opinions. 3) Exchange them with a partner or partners and have them determine whether the sentences are facts or opinions. Discuss what word or words in each sentence makes it a fact or an opinion.*

I.   Topic: _____

_____   1. _____

_____   2. _____

_____   3. _____

II. Topic: _____

_____   1. _____

_____   2. _____

_____   3. _____

III. Topic: _____

_____   1. _____

_____   2. _____

_____   3. _____

IV. Topic: _____

_____   1. _____

_____   2. _____

_____   3. _____

V.   Topic: _____

_____   1. _____

_____   2. _____

_____   3. _____

1-4 | Quoting, Paraphrasing, and Summarizing

Review

Avoid plagiarism.

Plagiarism is presenting others' ideas as your own. Plagiarizing is the theft of intellectual property and can have serious consequences. To avoid plagiarizing, (1) identify your sources in your notes so you know whose ideas you've written down, (2) document your sources in your paper using MLA or another documentation format, and (3) check your paper before turning it in to make sure you haven't plagiarized unintentionally.

Use quotations, paraphrases, and summaries to present other writers' ideas.

A **direct quotation** reproduces another author's exact words. Quoting can be a valuable way to convey or support a point, but you shouldn't rely on direct quotations to speak for you. Use a quotation only if rephrasing it would lessen the impact of the author's language and ideas. When quoting, follow these guidelines:

- Enclose the quotation in double quotation marks.
- Introduce the quotation with an appropriate signal phrase.
- Discuss or interpret the quotation so the reader understands its meaning and significance.
- Include source information in the Works Cited or References page and an in-text citation.

  Example of a quotation: In the prologue to his book *The Great Dissent*, Thomas Healy characterizes Justice Holmes's dissent in *Abrams v. United States* as "the most important minority opinion in American legal history" (8).

A **paraphrase** is a restatement of an author's ideas in your own words and style. It's about the same length as the author's original wording and preserves the author's tone and point of view. When paraphrasing, follow these guidelines:

- Make sure you understand the author's meaning.
- When paraphrasing, don't look at the original words so you don't inadvertently copy them.
- Clearly separate your opinions from the author's.
- Include source information in the Works Cited or References page and an in-text citation.

A **summary** also conveys an author's ideas in your own words. When you summarize, you state the author's main ideas and explain how they relate to one another. A summary preserves the author's tone and point of view, but it is much shorter than the original text. When summarizing, follow these guidelines:

- Make sure you understand the text thoroughly and accurately.
- Don't change the meaning of the original text.
- Avoid quoting the original text. Limit any necessary quotations to as few words as possible.
- Clearly separate your opinions from the author's.
- Include source information in the Works Cited or References page and an in-text citation.

Remember: Summarizing can be challenging and may require more than one attempt.

| **1-4a** | Quoting, Paraphrasing, and Summarizing |

Directions: *Read each passage and, without looking back at it, paraphrase each on a separate sheet. Next, write one sentence about each paragraph that incorporates a quote from the passage. Finally, use your paraphrase and quotes to develop a three-sentence summary for each passage.*

1. John B. Russworm was America's first black college graduate, and Samuel Cornish was a Presbyterian clergyman. Each man decided to take a stand against practices that seemed to mock the very face of the concept of justice and on which the nation was founded. It should also be reiterated that Russworm's and Cornish's educational backgrounds play a large role in their abilities to document the happenings of the time. An education for men of color took on a totally different connotation when viewed within the context of social limitations and low social expectations unduly leveed on any and all black people of the period being examined. Hence, with less than half a century since the freeing of slaves, it was no less than a feat of amazement for any African-American to be able to accomplish any type of social or civil expression during the pre-Civil War era.

    Quoted sentence: _____

    Summary: _____

    _____

    _____

2. The Negro press was one of the very few ways that Blacks could find some semblance of solace from a social structure that doomed them at birth. The notion that abolition could come to fruition must have also been as unfathomable to the minds of the Black masses as being freed from bondage sailed back to Africa. Nevertheless, the Negro press sallied forth, undaunted by the insurmountable odds, towards a better tomorrow. In doing so, it recorded each miniscule step made towards justice and equality. The documentation of such a herculean effort was not guided by a neatly cropped path lined by aromatic flowers. Instead, it was outlined by a dust covered road filled with potholes and bordered by the elongated figures of men and women who had been lynched and now hang rocking gently from a tree as each breeze nudges their lifeless bodies with a condescending gentle push. However, sans the black press, such information would have lost or obscured to degree that would bastardize the truth.

    Quoted sentence: _____

    Summary: _____

    _____

    _____

| **1-4b** | Quoting, Paraphrasing, and Summarizing |

Directions: *Read the original text below. Write one sentence incorporating a quotation from the paragraph using an attribution phrase. Then, write a sentence-by-sentence paraphrase and a one sentence summary.*

Tobacco Products

Should tobacco products be banned? Well, many people believe that tobacco is dangerous. In fact, they think that it causes a lot of problems to the average body. These problems can include breathing issues, bad breath, and cancer. The nicotine in tobacco products has been linked to several illnesses. Nicotine is a substance that coats the lungs and other organs necessary to breathe with millions of carcinogens. Carcinogens are cancer causing agents that are frequently found in many chemicals. Therefore, tobacco should be banned because it detrimentally affects breathing, contains nicotine, and introduces carcinogens into the body that cause cancer.

—D. Lewis

1. Write one quote from the paragraph.

   _____

   _____

   _____

   _____

2. Paraphrase the paragraph.

   _____

   _____

   _____

   _____

3. Summarize the paragraph.

   _____

   _____

   _____

   _____

1-4c | Quoting, Paraphrasing, and Summarizing

Directions: *Divide into groups of three. Each group member should select a different paragraph from below. On separate paper, write a one-sentence summary of the paragraph that you have selected. Pass your summary to a group member, who will paraphrase it. Finally, pass the summary and paraphrase to the other group member, who will check them against the paragraph to see if they are accurate. Rewrite any that are not.*

Paragraph 1

Change agents are those who act as proponents for the adoption of new ideas. The successful implementation of ideas can also be said to have more importance than the idea itself. Moreover, five adoption profiles are argued to exist in all organizations and cultures: (1) innovators, (2) early adopters, (3) members of the early majority, (4) members of the late majority, and (5) laggards. Each adoption profile can be identified by specific characteristics. For example, innovators are adventuresome; early adopters are respected; early majority interact frequently with peers for data; late majority are skeptical; and laggards are suspicious. The two former profiles are thought to be change agents. They are said to be such because they can influence clients' innovation-decisions per their change agency (organization for which the change agent operates). In fact, change agents are the catalyst that prompted the development of the Internet and its current level of success.

Paragraph 2

Today, sugar sweetened beverages are more available to impressionable, or easily influence, groups. Children and people who suffer from a general lack of self-control can too easily acquire sugar sweetened beverages. To tempt individuals who may not possess the self-restraint to not over indulge in detrimental, but seemingly harmless, behavior is no less than criminal (or at the very least indicates a lack of civic responsibility). Thus, there is a need to draft a law that holds the seller responsible to a certain extent for the excessive selling and/or promotion of an item that is obviously not to the benefit of the consumer.

Paragraph 3

English 131 online gives students the rare opportunity to be able to speak their minds sans the fear of peer pressure. The class includes discussion boards and group assignments that force students to really scrutinize the works of others. Most students are not comfortable with critiquing other students in a traditional class. However, the anonymity of the discussion boards provides the perfect platform to say what one really thinks. First year students are looking to develop their own voices. The discussion boards are a fantastic proving ground to hone one's writing skills to a razor-sharp edge, which allows for quick and accurate assessments. In fact, the atmosphere of the discussion boards is akin to encouragement session as opposed to a gladiatorial arena. Furthermore, the diversity of the writing styles and variances of ideas are fertile soil for the planting of new understanding as one ventures forth into the very bowels of academia.

2-1	Understanding Writing Assignments

Review

Consider the context, purpose, and audience of the text you are going to write.

Context refers to the circumstances surrounding your assignment—usually your class, the instructor's expectations, and the discipline. Different disciplines often use different formats. For instance, a history professor may ask you to write an essay comparing and contrasting the platforms of two political parties in 1860, while a biology professor may ask you to write a report on an experiment.

A text's **purpose** is the reason it is written—to persuade, report, or analyze, for instance. The purpose should be clear in your thesis. Remember to provide evidence to support your argument or the credibility of your information.

The **audience** of a text is its intended reader. Think about what your instructor hopes to learn from reading the assignment. For example, one reason your instructor is reading your paper to find out how well you understand the topic. Unless your professor specifies a different audience, think of your audience as an educated layperson. Include sufficient background and remember to define specialized terms. Your tone should probably be somewhat formal.

Read and analyze the assignment.

Look for directives and key words, as well as technical requirements, due dates, and other important information.

Directives are verbal statements that tell you what to write about and how to write about it. Common directives are *analyze*, *argue*, *explain*, *compare*, *contrast*, and *evaluate*. Pay attention to how many directives there are in an assignment.

> Example of an assignment with two directives: Identify and explain four traits of pre–World War I Europe that led to the outbreak of the war.

Look for key words. **Key words** specify what to include in your answer. In the directive above, the key words are "four traits." You will not identify events, but characteristics. You will also need to explain how each of these characteristics caused European countries to go to war.

Also look for other important details:

- Due date: Find and make a note of the date the assignment is due.
- Stages: Your instructor may require you to turn in various stages of your assignment, such as an outline, a bibliography of your sources, or a draft.
- Format: This may include text length, page and font requirements, or documentation style, such as MLA or APA.
- Submission method: Your instructor may want you to hand in the paper during class, e-mail it, or submit it through an online forum.

If the assignment doesn't include all the information you need, ask your instructor for clarification.

2-1a	Understanding Writing Assignments

Directions: *Explain what is expected from students based on the underlined word in each prompt.*

1. In a well-developed essay, <u>explore</u> the concept of love.

   _____

2. <u>Explain</u> the concept of love in a well-developed essay.

   _____

3. Using the articles from the course, <u>define</u> the concept of love in a well-developed essay.

   _____

4. <u>Discuss</u> the concept of love as it is represented in pop culture, in a well-developed essay.

   _____

5. In class, we've looked at how love is represented in Top 40 music charts. <u>Summarize</u> the concept of love based upon the Top 40 music charts in a well-developed essay.

   _____

6. <u>Outline</u>, in a well-developed essay, the concept of love.

   _____

7. Based on class discussions, <u>illustrate</u> the concept of love in a well-developed essay.

   _____

8. Through the format of a well-developed essay, <u>analyze</u> the concept of love.

   _____

9. <u>Prove</u> the concept of unconditional love from a parent, in a well-developed essay.

   _____

10. Taking into consideration the poems of various authors, <u>evaluate</u> the concept of love in a well-developed essay.

    _____

11. <u>Contrast</u> the concepts of love and hate in a well-developed essay.

    _____

12. <u>Demonstrate</u> the concept of love in a well-developed essay.

    _____

2-1b | Understanding Writing Assignments

Directions: *Please read the passage below and answer the questions that follow.*

Assignment 1: Argumentative Essay

Directions: *Based on the prompt, write a well-developed, expository essay in third person; use MLA formatting.*

Many people suffer from smoking-related illnesses. The prevalence of these ailments, regardless of the abundance of preventative campaigns against smoking, continues to increase annually and leads, unfortunately, to the untimely deaths of thousands of people. Therefore, politicians have recently proposed a law banning the sale of cigarettes. **In a well-supported essay, argue for or against the banning of tobacco products.**

1. What is the purpose of the assignment?

   _____

   _____

2. What word(s) in the prompt indicate the purpose of the assignment?

   _____

   _____

3. What is the topic of the essay?

   _____

   _____

Assignment 2: Annotated Bibliography

Directions: *Create an MLA-style Works Cited page of twenty or more scholarly sources using your library's database. For each source, write a paragraph-long annotation (approximately five sentences) summarizing the source. At least five sources must be print-based.*

1. How many sources are required?

   _____

2. May the sources come from the Internet?

   _____

3. What is the purpose of the assignment?

   _____

2-1c | Understanding Writing Assignments

Directions: *Read the following prompts. In your own words, write down what the assignment is asking you to do. Mark the word or words in each paragraph that help you understand the assignment. Exchange your interpretation of the directions with a classmate and discuss the similarities and/or differences in your understandings.*

1. Read Flannery O'Connor's short story "A Good Man Is Hard to Find." In the story, there are several interesting characters. Each character's role in the story helps to build the development of the plot. It can be argued that the most polarizing of the characters is the grandmother. Her mannerisms and perspectives on the world are very rigid. Nonetheless, she provides a certain level of truthfulness and vulnerability. In the context of the period in which the work is set, critically examine the grandmother's behavior and determine whether it is a reflection or distortion of the prevailing public sentiment of the era.

   _____

   _____

   _____

   _____

2. Video games have become a huge industry. People of all ages enjoy gaming for recreation and, now, even see it as a viable means of employment. The video-gaming industry is so expansive that television shows are dedicated to the culture of gaming, and video games have been adapted into blockbuster films that generate billions of dollars in revenue. The scope of video games has also moved into the arena of education. Educational video games are not a new concept, but the degree to which they are being integrated into curricula has increased significantly. As video game technology continues to advance, it is important to consider the ramifications of the many uses of video games. Discuss whether you believe there are beneficial uses of video games in modern society.

   _____

   _____

   _____

   _____

3. An international water crisis is unfolding. It is imperative that measures are employed to address the lack of fresh water available for human consumption. Although efforts are well underway, public awareness of this issue needs to be increased because there is a limited amount of fresh water sources available around the globe. Describe feasible solutions to the global problem of diminishing sources of fresh water for the world's population.

   _____

   _____

   _____

   _____

| 2-2 | Understanding the Rhetorical Situation |

Review

Consider the rhetorical situation of your text.

A text's **rhetorical situation** includes its purpose, audience, and context. **Purpose** is what the text is supposed to accomplish. **Audience** is the type of people the text is meant to appeal to. **Context** is when and where the text is written and the larger conversation it belongs to.

Example of a rhetorical situation: A job application letter.

- Purpose: to inform the reader of your qualifications and convince the company to hire you. These are two closely-related purposes.
- Audience: a potential employer. This audience knows all about the job but nothing about you.
- Context: part of larger job search. Each application must be tailored to the job opening it addresses.

Identify your purpose for writing.

The most common purposes for writing are to inform, to persuade, to express, and to entertain. Each can include more specific purposes:

- An **informative text** might, for example, demonstrate, report, or exemplify.
- A **persuasive text** might justify, change readers' minds, or convince them to act.
- An **expressive text** communicates the writer's thoughts and feelings so readers can experience them vicariously and understand them.
- An **entertaining text** might make readers laugh, cry, or keep them in suspense.

Once you know your purpose, determine what tone to use. **Tone** is how you communicate your attitude toward your topic. Writers express tone through word choice and writing style.

Tailor your writing to your specific audience.

For most college assignments, your audience is your instructor and possibly your classmates. However, some assignments will ask you to write for other audiences, real or imagined. Determine how much your audience knows about your topic. If they know a lot, you don't have to provide as much background or define as many technical terms as you would if they were unfamiliar with it.

Find out if your audience agrees with your position on the topic. If they don't, you will need to use logical argument and irrefutable evidence to persuade them. If they do, you can rely more on emotional appeals to strengthen their agreement.

Consider the context for your writing.

Often this will mean being aware of the assignment parameters set by your professor. These parameters will probably include the length of your paper and its due date. But you also need to consider where your paper falls within the field. Find out what others have written about the topic, whether the research supports your opinions or not, and how your ideas contribute to the overall conversation.

2-2a | Understanding the Rhetorical Situation

Directions: *For each scenario, fill in the blanks with a context, writer, audience, purpose, and topic.*

Scenario 1: You have been given an assignment at work to justify the allocation of more funds for the research and development division of the company. However, the company is not doing well and may need to decrease the budget of another division if the request is met. As the lead of the project that the funds will be used for, it is your task to write a compelling argument to make such a difficult budgetaey decision. Your response should be professional and well-developed.

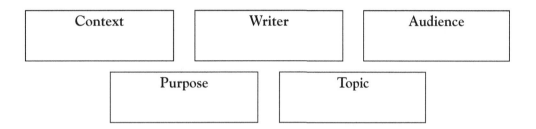

Scenario 2: In your Government 1301 course, you have been asked to read *The Declaration of Independence* and evaluate the relevance of its wording within a contemporary context. Your evaluation must reflect the ideas of constitutional law experts as noted in scholarly articles you have researched using the library's database.

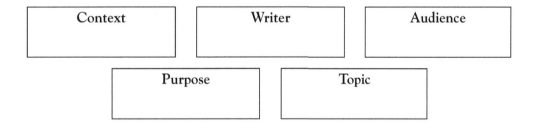

Scenario 3: You have been hired as a restaurant critic for the local newspaper. For your first column, you must review a new bistro and must include information about the chef, cuisine, and location of the establishment. Your review will be included as part of the newspaper's criteria for its Best Eateries list.

Context	Writer	Audience

Purpose	Topic

| **2-2b** | Understanding the Rhetorical Situation |

Directions: *For each prompt, underline the important details that help you to determine the rhetorical situation. Then, fill in the information based on what you have underlined.*

Prompt 1

The genre of action films has recently become extremely popular due to the success of several comic book-based blockbusters. Although most of the movies based on comic books have main characters who are fairly well known in pop culture, some of the newer films feature lesser-known characters, and many of these characters are minorities. The inclusion of minority superheroes reflects American diversity. These characters are indicative of a current social shift. Using scholarly articles to support your analysis, write an essay about a recent film adaptation that features a minority superhero, exploring the significance of the trend toward featuring minority hero types in terms of artistic social commentary.

Purpose: _____

Writer: _____

Subject: _____

Prompt 2

Learning to drive can be a joyous but frightening experience. No matter the learner's age, the process of becoming a competent, safe motorist is intense. For many generations, obtaining a driver's license was seen as a rite of passage into adulthood and people yearned to acquire a driver's license as soon as possible. However, today, many young individuals are opting to forgo, or delay indefinitely, the traditional practice of learning to drive and getting a driver's license. Within this context, construct a well-developed essay that discusses the impact on society of fewer people placing importance on driving.

Purpose: _____

Writer: _____

Subject: _____

Prompt 3

Illegal drug use and drug addictions are global concerns: Opiates and other narcotics plague cities on each continent. Write an essay from the point of view of a person recently released from prison for a nonviolent drug-related crime, listing the primary causes for illegal drug use.

Purpose: _____

Writer: _____

Subject: _____

2-2c	Understanding the Rhetorical Situation

Directions: *Divide into groups of three. Read the following passages. Each group member should complete one of the blanks (purpose, writer, subject). Based on the rhetorical situation, discuss the three aspects of the situation and decide together which word in each best describes the situation.*

Passage 1

A by-product of the Internet is the decentering of many aspects of the world. *Decentering* is the decentralization of data from one specific locale to several virtual locations. The government's decentering enables one to find government information online, monitor incoming information, bypass the traditional media, and engage in politics in digital provinces. The digital domain can also function as an anonymous distribution system for unsubstantiated information that would otherwise be deemed impermissible in official elections: Partisan websites, although inherently affiliated with certain candidates or parties, post unsubstantiated information without identifying direct connection to any liable parties. More importantly, decentralized governance of the nation gives Americans a true voice in its political system, which extends well beyond elections.

Purpose: _____

Writer: _____

Subject: _____

   Situations: Formal/Informal   Persuade/Inform/Entertain   Academic/Professional

Passage 2

Over the last few decades, sugar-sweetened beverage container size has increased, and, therefore, so has.consumers' intake of sugar-based calories. Just as sugary beverages' container size has increased, so has the consumption of high-calorie meals and snacks. If the federal government set a standard packaging size for sugar sweet beverages, it could yield immediate benefits for the public at large.

Purpose: _____

Writer: _____

Subject: _____

   Situations: Formal/Informal   Persuade/Inform/Entertain   Academic/Professional

Passage 3

Current research suggests that the way a person is reared directly impacts his or her ability to communicate effectively. Thus, language development is part cultural, or societal. If a person is reared in an environment that places strong emphasis on exchanging dialogue, then he or she will develop recognizable speech patterns. In turn, if one is raised in an environment where children are discouraged from verbal interaction with adults, then his or her language development is somewhat impeded, if not delayed.

Purpose: _____

Writer: _____

Subject: _____

2-3	Writing Thesis Statements

Review

Determine your topic and narrow it down.

The **general topic** of your essay is the general subject you will be writing about. Because an essay is short, you will have to narrow down your general topic.

Start by looking at your assignment. Your instructor may provide a tightly focused prompt, such as "Explain the stages in the life cycle of a butterfly." However, you will often be assigned a general topic, such as "Shakespeare's plays," and you must narrow it down so that you can discuss it thoroughly in just a few pages. Similarly, you may be asked to choose your own topic in a prompt such as "Analyze and evaluate a global organization." In these cases, you must not only pick the topic but also narrow it down.

Choose a topic that interests you.

To choose your own topic, think about what matters to you. Do you have a passionate interest or a pet peeve? Is there something you would like to see improved or changed? Have you recently learned something new and interesting that you'd like to learn more about?

To narrow down your topic, generate subtopics. There are several ways to do so:

- Freewrite: Spend 10 to 15 minutes writing down everything you can think of about your topic.
- Cluster: Create an idea web of subtopics around your topic, clustering related ideas around the subtopics.
- Brainstorm: List all the subtopics you can think of that relate to your topic.
- Ask a reporter's questions: Ask and answer questions about your topic, such as *who, what, when, where, why,* and *how.*

Your next task is to use the ideas you've generated to narrow down your topic. First, select two or three closely related subtopics that interest you. Then, formulate a narrow topic that encompasses all of them, such as "the pitfalls of relying on Internet-enabled cottage industries in the twenty-first century."

Write a thesis statement about your narrow topic.

A **thesis statement** introduces your topic and sets a direction for your essay. Start by creating a research question about your narrow topic. Next, do some research to find an answer. Then, put the answer into the form of a thesis statement.

An effective thesis statement has certain characteristics:

- It includes your critical opinion on the topic.
- It suggests the evidence you will use in the essay.
- It is arguable rather than a statement of universally accepted fact or belief.

Example of a thesis statement: Eliot's masterful use of literary, biblical, historical, and cultural allusion in "The Waste Land" allows his exploration of personal and generational disillusionment to transcend time and place.

2-3a	Writing Thesis Statements

Directions: *Fill in the blanks.*

1. **Essay question:** Why should all people love each other? (In a five-paragraph essay, explain.)

Your three main points:

a) _____

b) _____

c) _____

Your thesis statement:

_____

_____

2. **Essay question:** What does the introduction of a five-paragraph essay consist of?

Your three main points:

a) _____

b) _____

c) _____

Your thesis statement:

_____

_____

3. **Essay question:** How can a person increase his or her vocabulary and range of verbal styles in everyday language?

Your three main points:

a) _____

b) _____

c) _____

Your thesis statement:

_____

_____

2-3b	Writing Thesis Statements

Directions: *For each topic, create a thesis statement based on the supporting points listed.*

Topic 1: Self-driving cars

1. Automobiles' operational systems are basically complex computers.

2. Millennials are not interested in learning to drive.

3. Human-caused auto accidents are at an all-time high.

Your thesis statement:

_____

_____

Topic 2: Traveling

1. Trips provide exposure to different cultures.

2. Visiting new places offers opportunities to interact immersively and in real life, in foreign languages.

3. Sightseeing provides a chance to understand the function of famous locations.

Your thesis statement:

_____

_____

Topic 3: Attending college

1. A degree allows for better employment opportunities.

2. Post-secondary education bestows useful knowledge.

3. Higher education is a way to become more civically engaged.

Your thesis statement:

_____

_____

2-3c	Writing Thesis Statements

Directions: *Divide into groups. For each prompt, each group member fills in one blank with a main point. Then, as a group, use the points to develop a thesis that addresses the essay question.*

1. **Essay prompt:** Should America continue to explore space for other life forms?

Your three main points:

a) The universe is vast and holds lots to be discovered

b) Other life forms may have technology that can benefit mankind

c) The world can unite for a common goal

Your thesis statement:

With the uncharted vastness of the universe, we as a society should entertain exploration to benefit humankind.

2. **Essay prompt:** Justify the medicinal use of marijuana and other plants that have narcotic properties.

Your three main points:

a) Marijuana has been used for medicinal purposes for 1000's of years.

b) The pharmaceutical companies have suppressed this form of therapy.

c) Marijuana laws were constructed by racist in the 30's and propelled by christian ideology.

Your thesis statement:

With the suppression of Marijuana as a medicinal plant, a new examination needs to implemented

3. **Essay prompt:** How can a person earn a college degree in four years or less? Explain.

Your three main points:

a) _____

b) _____

c) _____

Your thesis statement:

_____

_____

2-4 | Organizing Your Essay

Review

Use description to support a dominant impression.

Description uses vivid sensory details. Organize your description spatially, chronologically, or by importance. For example, you might describe parking garage with words that suggest creepiness.

Use narration to support a point.

Narration tells a story in chronological or time order. You might use it to describe the events of a significant battle.

Use illustration to explain a topic or support a claim.

Illustration involves providing concrete, specific examples to support a topic or claim and is organized in order of importance. You might use illustration when discussing a poet's use of simile.

Use the process pattern to explain how something works or how to do something.

A process essay is organized chronologically, beginning with the first step and ending with the last. You would use the process pattern to explain how medieval painters made and applied gesso.

Use definition to explain the meaning of a term or concept.

Definitions generally divide a term into subcategories. A definition often includes description, illustration, and comparison and contrast. You might use definition to explore the meaning of *success*.

Use comparison and contrast to explore similarities and differences.

You can compare and/or contrast people, ideas, or things. Comparing means examining similarities; contrasting involves looking at differences. You might compare and contrast a control group with an experimental group in a drug trial.

Use cause and effect to describe logical connections between events.

Cause is why something happened, and effect is the result of an action. You might analyze the effects of a gas leak.

Use classification to divide topics into simpler subtopics.

Use categorical organization to classify your topic based on purpose and audience. You might classify businesses as sole proprietorships, partnerships, corporations, or limited liability companies.

Use argument to persuade readers to agree with your position or take a certain action.

An argument centers on a debatable and reasonable position and is often organized by importance, with the most important argument at the end. An effective argument anticipates counterarguments.

2-4a | Organizing Your Essay

Directions: *Read the prompt and fill in the blanks below to begin to develop the thesis statement and topic sentences for the body of an essay.*

Essay Prompt: If it were possible to create a time machine, how could the machine be used to benefit humanity?

Thesis: _____

_____

Body Paragraph 1 Topic Sentence: _____

Major Detail _____

Minor Detail _____

Major Detail _____

Minor Detail _____

Major Detail _____

Body Paragraph 2 Topic Sentence: _____

Major Detail _____

Minor Detail _____

Major Detail _____

Minor Detail _____

Major Detail _____

Body Paragraph 3 Topic Sentence: _____

Major Detail _____

Minor Detail _____

Major Detail _____

Minor Detail _____

Major Detail _____

2-4b   Organizing Your Essay

Directions: *Answer the following questions.*

1. **Thesis:** *Pollution is a global concern that has impacted major industries including, fishing, oil exploration, and ground transportation.*

    a.   What is the topic of the thesis? _____

    b.   What are the points of development? _____

    c.   Based on the thesis, what will the topic be for body paragraph 2? _____

2. **Topic Sentence:** *The rising cost of sugar is directly correlated to the low rain levels of the past two years.*

    a.   What is the topic of the topic sentence? _____

    b.   What is the point of development? _____

    c.   Write a supporting detail that reinforces the topic sentence. _____

    _____

3. **Thesis:** *High unemployment, increasing high school dropout rates, and a surge in illegal drug use are attributable reasons for America's high crime rates.*

    a.   What is the topic of the thesis? _____

    b.   What are the points of development? _____

    c.   Develop a restatement of the thesis statement that reflects the same ideas as the thesis. _____

4. Indicate where each of the following sentences belongs.

| Clincher | Thesis | Topic Sentence |
| Title | Hook | Restatement of Thesis |

INTRODUCTION   **BODY**   **CONCLUSION**

_____   _____   _____

_____   _____   _____

_____   _____   _____

2-4c | Organizing Your Essay

Directions: *Divide into groups of three. Work together to determine a title and thesis that address the below prompt. Write three topic sentences. Then, on separate paper, each person writes one body paragraph. Work together to determine a logical conclusion. Finally, on separate paper, combine all paragraphs to form a complete essay.*

Essay Prompt: If a person could have superpowers, what would they be and why?

Title: _____

Thesis: _____

_____

Body Paragraph 1 Topic Sentence:

_____

_____

Body Paragraph 2 Topic Sentence:

_____

_____

Body Paragraph 3 Topic Sentence:

_____

_____

Conclusion

_____Summarize Body 1 Detail

_____

_____Summarize Body 2 Detail

_____

_____Summarize Body 3 Detail

_____

| 2-5 | Writing Introductions and Conclusions |

Review

Begin your essay with an interesting and thought-provoking introduction.

An effective introduction makes your audience want to keep reading. It hooks readers' interest, indicates the topic, builds a point of view, and avoids generalizations or announcements. Here are five strategies for hooking your readers from the first sentence:

- Start with an anecdote. Telling a story adds interest, provides context, and can evoke sympathy.
- Give an overview of the topic to provide background information and context to help readers understand your discussion. An overview can include definitions of unfamiliar or abstract topics.
- Begin with a relevant and interesting quotation. This shows your topic is part of a larger conversation. When you use a quotation, make sure that you understand it correctly, place it in context, and connect it to your own ideas.
- State an interesting fact or statistic. This tactic not only hooks the reader, but also lends credibility to your essay.
- Ask a question that will get readers to start thinking about the topic. You can use the question to build to a thesis suggesting an answer.

There is no single type of introduction that will work for all papers. Think about which will be most effective for your topic, purpose, and audience.

End your essay with a memorable conclusion.

An effective conclusion sticks in your readers' memory and offers closure or a final thought on the topic. Here are five strategies for leaving your readers with a lasting impression:

- Reference the introduction. You might, for instance, tell how an opening anecdote ended or answer a question you asked in the first line. This gives a satisfying sense of closure.
- Restate the thesis in different words. This will emphasize your main point.
- End with a call to action, a proposal, or a suggestion. This tactic works well after an argument intended to encourage readers to get up and take action.
- Close with a provocative or rhetorical question. This is good way to end a persuasive essay because it prompts readers to keep thinking about the points you've made or solutions you've proposed.
- Summarize your key points. This is a useful strategy for longer papers, when you want to remind readers of the ideas and evidence you've presented. It's too repetitive for shorter papers, however.

2-5a	Writing Introductions and Conclusions

Directions: *Create an Introduction and Conclusion based on the following essay prompt.*
Prompt: "In a five-paragraph essay, explain why all people should love each other."

Introduction Paragraph

_____

Hook *(attention-getter):* _____

Thesis statement *(incorporate your three main points of support):* _____

_____

Write the **Introduction** following the list below:

_____(Hook)

_____(General Information)

_____(Reason)

_____(Explanation of Reason)

_____(Thesis)

Conclusion Paragraph

Write the **Conclusion** following the list below:

_____ (Restatement of Thesis)

_____ (Summarize First Main Point)

_____ (Summarize Second Main Point)

_____(Summarize Third Main Point)

_____(Clincher)

| **2-5b** | Writing Introductions and Conclusions |

Directions: *Put the scrambled sentences in the correct order to form a well-developed Introduction and Conclusion. Then, rewrite the paragraphs on a separate sheet of paper.*

Introduction

1. _____   **a.** The nicotine in tobacco products has been linked to several illnesses.

2. _____   **b.** Therefore, tobacco should be banned because it detrimentally affects breathing, contains nicotine, and introduces carcinogens into the body.

3. _____   **c.** Should tobacco products be banned?

4. _____   **d.** These problems can include breathing issues, bad breath, and cancer.

5. _____   **e.** Well, many people believe that tobacco is dangerous.

6. _____   **f.** In fact, they think that it causes a lot of problems to the average body.

7. _____   **g.** Carcinogens are cancer-causing agents present in many chemicals.

8. _____   **h.** Nicotine is a substance that coats the lungs and other organs necessary to breathe with millions of carcinogenic compounds.

Conclusion

1. _____   **a.** It weakens the immune system and makes people more susceptible to sicknesses.

2. _____   **b.** Since tobacco affects breathing, contains nicotine, and introduces carcinogens into the body, it should definitely be banned.

3. _____   **c.** These carcinogens increase the probability of a person developing cancer by more than 50%.

4. _____   **d.** Thus tobacco should be banned because its use has many negative consequences.

5. _____   **e.** Moreover, the nicotine in tobacco is a substance that drastically increases the possibility of acquiring numerous illnesses.

6. _____   **f.** Also, carcinogens are introduced through tobacco via nicotine and other chemicals used to make many tobacco products.

7. _____   **g.** It blocks the airway with tar that builds up after tobacco use.

8. _____   **h.** In other words, tar slowly accumulates in the throat and lungs, which prevents the flow of oxygen.

2-5c	Writing Introductions and Conclusions

Directions: *Divide into groups. Sit in a circle. Fill in the blanks in numerical order moving in a clockwise pattern.*

Question: *Should students be mandated to attend school all 12 months?*

Introduction Paragraph

Hook *(attention-getter):* _____

Thesis statement *(incorporate your three main points of support):*

_____

_____

Write the **Introduction** following the list below:

_____(Hook)

_____(General Information)

_____(Reason)

_____(Explanation of Reason)

_____(Thesis)

Conclusion Paragraph

Write the **Conclusion following the liste below:**

_____(Restatement of Thesis)

_____(Summarize First Main Point)

_____(Summarize Second Main Point)

_____(Summarize Third Main Point)

_____(Clincher)

3-1 | Writing Topic Sentences

Review

Every good paragraph has three things:

- a topic—the general idea of the paragraph
- a topic sentence—a sentence that makes your point about the topic and controls the ideas and structure of the paragraph. The topic sentence may be implied.
- supporting details—specifics that explain or prove the topic sentence

Write your thesis statement first.

Begin by researching your topic. Then, create a thesis statement that states what your essay is about and makes a point about it. A good thesis statement also suggests a structure for your essay.

> Example of a **thesis statement**: New York City and Los Angeles are both large cosmopolitan American cities with rich cultural offerings, but for tourists, their differing histories, geographies, and architectures create two very different experiences.

Generate a central idea for each paragraph.

Each central idea should expand on and support your thesis statement. It will confuse readers if the topics of your paragraphs don't support your thesis statement. To come up with central ideas, use methods such as questioning, clustering, listing, and freewriting.

Use topic sentences to achieve the goals of the thesis statement.

Create a topic sentence for each central idea. Test each one against the thesis statement to make sure it follows the plan the statement suggests for the essay. Remember that your topic sentence shouldn't just introduce the paragraph's topic. It should also let the reader know what structure the paragraph is likely to follow. A topic sentence is often, but not always, the first sentence in a paragraph.

> Example of a **topic sentence**: New York City crowds onto islands and peninsulas, while Los Angeles sprawls between the mountains and the sea.

Use a topic sentence to provide a structure for the supporting details.

Decide which supporting details you can use to develop the points made in each of the topic sentences. Again, test each detail against the topic sentence to make sure it is relevant.

> Example of relevant **supporting details**: New York City is approximately 300 square miles with over 8.5 million people; Los Angeles is approximately 500 square miles with under 4 million people.

Check your paragraphs to make sure they support your thesis statement.

One method of confirming everything in your essay works together is to form a question from your thesis statement. Then, check to make sure each topic sentence provides a relevant answer to the question. Finally, check each paragraph to make sure every detail provides relevant support for the topic sentence.

3-1a	Writing Topic Sentences

1. **Directions:** *Read the following introduction, underline the thesis, and write three topic sentences based on the thesis.*

Introduction

Which is the best state in the United States to live in? When one thinks about moving or staying in a place, she may look for specific features that make a location desirable. The desired features vary from person to person, but there are general aspects of states that act as important factors in determining the feasibility of uprooting one's life and starting anew in unfamiliar surroundings. These factors may range from crime rates to access to outdoor spaces. In other words, the designation of such an important determination includes both intrinsic and extrinsic factors. Despite the broadness of the query, one can easily argue that Texas is the best state to live in, due to its economy, affordable housing, and relatively low crime rate.

Based on the introduction, what is the topic of the essay? _____

Topic Sentence 1: _____

Topic Sentence 2: _____

Topic Sentence 3: _____

2. **Directions:** *Write topic sentences for each of the thesis statements.*

a. Everyone should have an annual check-up with a physician for illness prevention, illness intervention, and mental health screening.

Topic Sentence 1: _____

Topic Sentence 2: _____

Topic Sentence 3: _____

b. Cell phones have become an essential aspect of modern living due to many reasons.

Topic Sentence 1: _____

Topic Sentence 2: _____

Topic Sentence 3: _____

3-1b	Writing Topic Sentences

1. **Directions:** *Review these vague sentences and rewrite them so they are clear and concise topic sentences.*

   a. The cake is good.

   _____

   b. Terry is a bad man.

   _____

2. **Directions:** *Develop a thesis statement for each topic and write three topic sentences for each thesis statement.*

   a. **Topic:** Video Games

   Thesis: Video Games are a distraction from reality.

   Topic Sentence 1: Video Games have a distinct negative impact on society

   Topic Sentence 2: Video Games create an artificial sense of accomplishments

   Topic Sentence 3: Video Games contribute to the errosion of intellegence.

   b. **Topic:** Unemployment

   Thesis: _____

   Topic Sentence 1: _____

   Topic Sentence 2: _____

   Topic Sentence 3: _____

   c. **Topic:** Value of Multiculturalism

   Thesis: Multiculturalism is being systematically destroyed by PC culture

   Topic Sentence 1: Due to current values climates, multiculturism is being eroded.

   Topic Sentence 2: The misunderstanding of various cultures leads to violence.

   Topic Sentence 3: White culture has been pushing their values on others and has a severe impact

| **3-1c** | Writing Topic Sentences |

Directions: *Find a partner or partners and use the thesis statements below to develop topic sentences as a group. Be sure to check for consistency between the topic sentences. Use a dictionary to help define any unfamiliar words.*

1. Alcoholism negatively impacts families in several ways.

    a. Topic Sentence 1: _____

    b. Topic Sentence 2: _____

    c. Topic Sentence 3: _____

2. Recreational marijuana use has been approved in some states due to economics, crime rates, and medical applications.

    a. Topic Sentence 1: _____

    b. Topic Sentence 2: _____

    c. Topic Sentence 3: _____

3. Infidelity, money issues, and poor communication are the main causes of divorce in the United States.

    a. Topic Sentence 1: _____

    b. Topic Sentence 2: _____

    c. Topic Sentence 3: _____

4. Tobacco needs further regulation due to its impact on children, seniors, and the environment.

    a. Topic Sentence 1: _____

    b. Topic Sentence 2: _____

    c. Topic Sentence 3: _____

5. STEM majors have many high-paying career options.

    a. Topic Sentence 1: _____

    b. Topic Sentence 2: _____

    c. Topic Sentence 3: _____

6. Recidivism is a leading factor in the increasing number of trade programs offered in prisons.

    a. Topic Sentence 1: _____

    b. Topic Sentence 2: _____

    c. Topic Sentence 3: _____

3-2   Including Supporting Ideas

Review

Support your thesis statement and topic sentences with details.

A thesis statement or topic sentence only supplies the basic structure for an essay or paragraph. The details bring the topic to life. Choose the details that best suit your purpose, tone, and audience. The most common types of support are examples, facts and statistics, reasons, explanations, anecdotes, descriptions, steps and procedures, and quotations.

Generate ideas for how to support your thesis statement.

Create an outline for your essay by writing down the thesis statement and topic sentences. Then do some prewriting for each topic sentence. You can use one of these techniques: brainstorming, free-writing, clustering, or asking reporter's questions—*who, what, why, where,* and *how.* Write down all the ideas that occur to you. Afterward, select the ones that best support your topics and main idea.

If you need to do research for your essay, use the evidence you find as your support. The best place to start is with general sources, such as encyclopedias and online searches. After you have a general idea of what evidence is available, choose more targeted sources, such as books, journals, videos, and websites.

Make sure your evidence is credible and relevant.

Find up-to-date, reliable sources. Make sure you examine every point of view on your topic. Before investing the time to read every possible source, check abstracts, summaries, and tables of contents to see which sources will provide the most relevant information for your topic. Remember to document every source you use so you won't unintentionally plagiarize someone else's ideas.

Use supporting details to expand on your topic sentence.

The topic sentence acts as a controlling idea for a paragraph. In the paragraph, provide enough relevant details to support your topic sentence. Organize your supporting details clearly and logically, based on chronology, spatial arrangement, or relative importance. You might also organize them based on comparison and contrast or cause and effect. Be sure to use transition words and phrases to highlight how the details connect to one another.

> Examples of **transition words and phrases**: *as a result, because, for example, however, in addition, in contrast, moreover, nevertheless, similarly,* and *yet*

Make sure your details support your thesis statement.

Remember that your thesis statement is the main idea of your essay. The topic sentences and supporting details are there as support for your thesis. Make sure each topic sentence and detail clearly support the thesis statement.

3-2a	Including Supporting Ideas

Directions: *Underline the topic and highlight the major detail that needs support. Then, develop supporting ideas based on the topic sentences and fill in the blanks.*

1. Drones are useful to the military–industrial complex. (*Topic Sentence*)

   a. _Drones can be unmanned._

   b. _Drones are cheaper than aircraft._

   c. _Drones can be more precise._

2. Across the globe, traditional zoo structures with caged animals have become controversial. (*Topic Sentence*)

   a. _____

   b. _____

   c. _____

3. As gun control laws are debated, Americans are negatively affected by gun violence. (*Topic Sentence*)

   a. _Gun violence has everlasting consequences._

   b. _Gun control laws need to be updated._

   c. _There is no debate in gun violence causing pain and sorrow._

4. First, many clothing brands use the same factories to produce their products. (*Topic Sentence*)

   a. _____

   b. _____

   c. _____

5. In addition, city planners are searching for creative ways to build in growing cities. (*Topic Sentence*)

   a. _____

   b. _____

   c. _____

6. Tons of food are thrown away while millions of people live in hunger in America. (*Topic Sentence*)

   a. _____

   b. _____

   c. _____

3-2b | Including Supporting Ideas

Directions: *Fill in the following blanks with points that support the topic sentence; be sure to use complete sentences.*

1. Bees are more important to everyday life than most people realize.

    a. _____

    b. _____

    c. _____

2. Professional sports produce some of the most influential figures in the world.

    a. _____

    b. _____

    c. _____

3. Today, children have more access to information than previous generations have had.

    a. _____

    b. _____

    c. _____

4. Depleting natural resources means the importance of renewable energy sources has increased.

    a. _____

    b. _____

    c. _____

5. The U.S. education system desperately needs more federal funding.

    a. _____

    b. _____

    c. _____

3-2c | Including Supporting Ideas

Directions: *Take five minutes to sort the scrambled words and phrases into Topic Sentences (TS) and Supporting Ideas. Compare your answers with partners and discuss reasons for your decisions.*

Laser discs	The three reasons I chose this school are:	
Multiple degree programs	Ensure food quality.	Pegasus
John	Journalism	Peaches
Glass bottles	FDA regulations protect the public in many ways.	Tin cans
English	Great professors	Bottling companies use different containers for water.
VHS tapes The School of Liberal Arts offers a number of programs.	Maria	Strawberries
Avoid food contamination.	Mohammed	History
Unicorns	Popular mythological creatures	Summer fruits
Across the globe, there are many common names.	Mermaids	
Plastic bottles Watermelon Low tuition	Prevent the use of harmful additives.	

TS: _____

Support 1: _____

Support 2: _____

Support 3: _____

TS: _____

Support 1: _____

Support 2: _____

Support 3: _____

TS: _____

Support 1: _____

Support 2: _____

Support 3: _____

TS: _____

Support 1: _____

Support 2: _____

Support 3: _____

TS: _____

Support 1: _____

Support 2: _____

Support 3: _____

TS: _____

Support 1: _____

Support 2: _____

Support 3: _____

3-3 | Writing Unified Paragraphs

Review

Develop a paragraph around only one main idea.

Don't go off topic. Going off topic can confuse readers.

Express your one main idea in the topic sentence.

Your topic sentence should state your topic and make a point about it.

> Example of a **topic sentence**: The first essential element in a healthy lifestyle is a balanced diet.

Here, the topic is the essential elements of a healthy lifestyle, and the specific point to be addressed in this paragraph is a balanced diet.

Support the main idea of the paragraph with details.

Think of all the details you can to support your topic sentence. Weigh them against both the main idea and the point you're making about it to make sure each is relevant.

> Examples of **supporting details**:
>
> - Vegetables supply fiber in addition to vitamins and minerals.
> - Protein is found in many foods, such as meats, dairy products, grains, and vegetables.
> - Even though it's healthy, some people do not enjoy the flavor of olive oil.

Eliminate sentences that do not support the main idea.

Check your paragraph to make sure every detail is clearly relevant to the point you're making in your topic sentence. Notice that the third detail above—about the flavor of olive oil—does not contribute to the notion of a balanced diet being part of a healthy lifestyle. That sentence should not be included in the paragraph.

3-3a | Writing Unified Paragraphs

Directions: *Read the paragraph. To identify the topic, circle the repeated word(s) or phrase(s) as you read. Once you have identified the topic, answer the questions that follow.*

(1) The concept of jealousy can be traced back as far as written language itself. (2) Some believe the concept has a Biblical origin, whereas more secular scholars tend to describe it as an innate trait of human beings. (3) Despite the possibly common origins, the concept of jealousy has been treated in many ways throughout history. (4) Envy is also a significant concern that is commonly focused on. (5) One can say that jealousy may be deemed the cause of conflict, a motivating factor for human interaction, and a universal theme in literature.

1. What is the topic of the paragraph? _____

2. What is the purpose of the paragraph? _____

3. Identify the sentence that expresses the main idea.

   _____

4. Which sentence does not belong? Why? _____

5. Rewrite the sentence that does not belong so it expresses unity with the topic.

   _____

(1) Jealousy causes conflict. (2) History is rife with instances of jealousy causing problems. (3) _____, it is not uncommon for siblings to fight with one another over an item that one has, and the other wants. (4) Although it can be argued that the such an altercation stems from deep-rooted issues, the fact still remains that jealousy is the triggering reason. (5) _____. (6) A fight between most siblings over material items can definitely be placed within the aforementioned parameter. (7) Therefore, it can also be said that jealousy can prompt one to act.

6. What transition can be added to sentence 2 to help unify the ideas? Why?

   _____

7. What is another word or words that can replace *jealousy* in sentence 4 while keeping the paragraph's meaning?

   _____

8. Write a sentence for *sentence 5* that maintains the coherence of the paragraph.

   _____

3-3b | Writing Unified Paragraphs

Directions: *Read the following paragraphs. Identify the sentences that are unnecessary.*

1.

The Development of Civilization

(1) In exploring the development of modern social infrastructure, Mesopotamia cannot be ignored as a major contributing factor to current notions of civilization. (2) Civilization, specifically urban civilization, can be defined as an advanced stage of development in human interaction. (3) Computers are important to social progress, but they did not exist during the height of Mesopotamia. (4) For any civilization to thrive, several components are needed; one of these is an ample supply of water. (5) To this end, it should be noted that the name *Mesopotamia,* from the Greek, means "between the rivers" — the Tigris and Euphrates rivers. (6) People loved to boat down the river. (7) Crucially, that civilization possessed one of the required physical attributes for the founding of a society. (8) However, as the basic needs of a society are met, more complex aspects of a civilization begin to emerge, including laws, art, and religion.

    a.   What is the topic of the paragraph? _____

    b.   Which sentence(s) is (are) unnecessary? _____

2.

(1) Raphael's The School of Athens and Popes' and Cardinals' use of art provide great insight into the intellectual process that is both encouraged and suppressed during the High Renaissance. (2) Intellectualism, over time, emerges as a means of interpreting life during the High Renaissance. (3) Raphael's fresco captures the High Renaissance from a vantage point that is both idealist and rational. (4) The work is set within a Roman bath house, which is regarded as a center of various endeavors. (5) Furthermore, philosophers flank each side of the work. (6) Their presence visually balances the fresco, a balance of understanding that cannot be fully understood. (7) It would probably be a great work of art for a private collector of Renaissance pieces. (8) Hence, the ideal of the continual search for truth becomes the unpainted central focus of the work. (9) The cast of characters that surrounds this focal point, including Alexander the Great, Minerva, and Apollo, symbolically forms the outer layers of the world on which all people tread throughout the cycle of life. (10) Again, one cannot forget that these layers surround, or protect, the truth from being tainted by outside forces. (11) Onions also have layers and were very widely available for consumption during Raphael's life. (12) Moreover, the elaborate works of art commissioned by high-ranking religious officials grant a corresponding glimpse into High Renaissance social order. (13) Those of affluence and influence emphasized their power, wealth, and superiority through ornate structures and paintings. (14) The justification for such adornment is that those closer to God should be seen a glorious light. (15) Thus, the artwork and architectural structures commissioned by Popes and Cardinals serve a dual purpose, a testament to their faith and an indicator of their wealth, power, and superiority.

    a.   What is the topic of the paragraph? _____

    b.   Write a title for the paragraph that indicates the main idea: _____

    c.   Which sentence(s) is(are) unnecessary? _____

3-3c | Writing Unified Paragraphs

Directions: *Work with a partner or partners to identify the topic and main idea of the paragraph. Recurring words or phrases by underlining them. Delete sentences that do not relate to the pattern of ideas.*

(1) Elites, in phase one, are normally the first to be introduced to a new technology, due to initial high costs. (2) Inflation increases the price of goods domestically traded. (3) This early level of use is often reserved for traditional power structures, such as government, military, higher education, and research and development organizations. (4) Following the innovation's experimental stages, new technology is presented to the public. (5) Video games gained popularity during the 1980s due to the development of home video game systems, such as Atari 2600. (6) Depending upon its acceptance or nonacceptance by the masses, the technology may be subjected to policies and enforcement to assist with its diffusion. (7) For example, the Internet finds its beginnings as a government project. (8) Each state has its own constitution besides the U.S. Constitution. (9) The government eventually pulls far enough away from the Internet to allow for public use. (10) Although its actual acknowledgment as a viable resource cannot be predetermined, once released from the constraints of bureaucratic limitations, the Internet is afforded the opportunity to mature as it may. (11) There is a finite supply of natural resources, so society needs to be careful in how it uses them. (12) The successful acceptance of the technology by the masses marks its progression towards full adoption.

1. What is the topic of the paragraph? _____

2. Which sentence(s) is(are) irrelevant? _____

3. What would be a good title for the paragraph? _____

| **3-4** | Writing Coherent Paragraphs |

Review

Organize your ideas logically.

Three organizational patterns are the most common:

- Chronological order: Also known as *time order*, this pattern tells events in the order in which they happen. Use chronological order to tell stories, explain events, or describe processes.
- Spatial order: Use this pattern to provide a three-dimensional picture for your reader. You can describe your subject from top to bottom, front to back, or one side to another.
- Order of importance: This pattern usually builds to the most important point and is particularly effective in arguments.

Use transitions to connect ideas.

Transitions can be words or phrases. They connect ideas by emphasizing how the ideas relate to one another. Here are some examples of transitions:

- Addition: *and, in addition, moreover, similarly*
- Cause/effect: *as a result, because, (in order) to, so that*
- Contrast: *even though, nevertheless, yet*
- Illustration: *including, namely, such as*

Use key words, synonyms, and pronouns to connect ideas.

Repeating key words ensures readers know what you're writing about. However, using the same key word over and over can become repetitious. To keep your writing interesting and effective, use synonyms and pronouns to avoid constant repetition.

Compare these two paragraphs:

A unique early-20th-century architectural style was **Mayan Revival. Mayan Revival** was particularly popular in the 1920s and 1930s. The architecture and imagery of pre-Columbian cultures in Mexico and Central America inform **Mayan Revival** buildings. A **Mayan Revival** building is the oddly named Aztec Hotel on the legendary Route 66. One of the best-known architects working in **Mayan Revival** was Frank Lloyd Wright. Wright designed the often filmed Ennis House in Los Angeles in **Mayan Revival**.

A unique early-20th-century architectural style was **Mayan Revival. It** was particularly popular in the 1920s and 1930s. The architecture and imagery of pre-Columbian cultures in Mexico and Central America inform Mayan Revival buildings, **such as** the oddly named Aztec Hotel on the legendary Route 66. One of the best-known architects working in **this style** was Frank Lloyd Wright, whose often filmed Ennis House in Los Angeles **recalls a Mayan temple**.

Notice how often *Mayan Revival*—a key term since it is the topic of the paragraph—is repeated in the paragraph on the left. On the right, though, it is replaced in a variety of ways: by the pronoun *it*, the transition *such as*, the phrase *this style*, and the restatement *recalls a Mayan temple*.

3-4a   Writing Coherent Paragraphs

I. **Directions:** *Read each paragraph. Insert the appropriate transition word or phrase into each blank to develop a coherent paragraph.*

Transitions			
Thus	For instance	However	Consequently

The concept of jealousy acts as a catalyst for social interaction. When a person becomes jealous, he or she often manifests his or her feelings in an aggressive manner. **(a)** _____, this expression of jealousy can lead to verbal conflicts or even physical confrontations. **(b)**_____, the interaction caused by jealousy does not have to solely take on negative connotations. **(c)** _____, a person may be jealous of a classmate's grades. This jealousy may prompt the jealous person to work harder and earn better grades in the class. **(d)** _____, it is quite obvious that the very nature of the word *jealousy* is an intrinsic aspect of writing.

Transitions				
Instead	For example	Again	Here	In other words

Adjustment to the multicultural way of life in the United Sates can be a daunting task for any person coming from a less-industrialized nation. In addition to the normal culture shock associated with any relocation to a new environment, a person seeking to increase his or her overall scholarly understanding within a formal setting faces an extremely complex, difficult feat. **(e)** _____, in addition to the anticipated unfamiliar environment and language barrier, finer nuances of the subcultures in America can only be fully comprehended connotatively. **(f)** _____, colloquialisms and figurative language can take on regional meanings that are easily misinterpreted by an ear unaccustomed to hearing certain words used within a context outside of their denotative meanings. A person may comment about another person's attire in the following manner: "You are hurting that outfit." **(g)** _____, the word *hurting* does not carry with its usual negative meaning. **(h)** _____, *hurting* is used as a way to state that the outfit is flattering. **(i)** _____, to one who has not been fully immersed in American culture, this type of situation poses a huge comprehension problem. If there is an issue with one's ability to comprehend, it undoubtedly will affect the individual's academic performance, regardless of his or her intellectual ability.

II. **Directions:** *On a separate sheet of paper, use the following transition words and phrases to write a coherent paragraph on the topic below.*

Transitions: In addition   Yet   On the other hand   Furthermore   Although
Topic: Performance-Enhancing Drugs in Sports

3-4b | Writing Coherent Paragraphs

Directions: *Identify the topic and the flaw that interferes with coherence, for each of the following paragraphs. On a separate sheet of paper, rewrite each paragraph to correct the problems; use at least one transition per sentence.*

_____ 1. Virtual Reality (VR) is a great tool in education. Nintendo makes fun games. VR has applications in science and history courses. Mario Brothers is the most iconic game for Nintendo. If a school adopts VR as part of its curriculum, then student engagement may increase significantly.

_____ 2. Unemployment in the United States is decreasing. Employers are hiring due to improved sales. Fewer people have jobs. If the unemployment rate continues to decrease, more people will not be able to pay for their living expenses. This is welcome news.

_____ 3. Traveling in foreign countries is an exciting experience. The price of oil is dropping due to the development of cleaner fuel alternatives. Solar energy is one of the many alternatives that companies are turning to. Eventually, oil reserves will be completely depleted, so it is vital that more countries begin to use alternative fuel sources.

_____ 4. Ice cream is the best dessert during the summer months. Whether it is in a cone or dish does not make any difference. Hot cocoa tastes like melted chocolate to some people. Vanilla is the most popular flavor sold around the world. More people should drink hot chocolate.

_____ 5. Being a police officer is a hard job. Identity theft is a major crime. When a criminal steals a person's identity, the damaging consequences to the crime victim can take years to repair. In some cases, the problems created are irreparable. Officers put their lives at risk each day.

_____ 6. Same-sex marriage has become a controversial issue across the nation. Many states recognize same-sex marriages. However, football is still America's most popular sport. These states allow the same privileges to same-sex couples as traditional couples. So, the question remains: Should football players be made to wear thicker helmets?

_____ 7. Pop music icons are always on television shows. A person's diet dictates, in part, his or her level of health. What an individual consumes has direct implications on his well-being. Poor eating habits often lead to becoming a pop icon. Therefore, people should be aware of their dietary practices if they want to be healthy.

_____ 8. Traffic jams have become a part of daily life in major cities. Cars emit a lot of fumes. Population density is a major factor for this road congestion. Another cause for clogs in traffic flow is that many people commute to work at the same times of day. If more fish is included in the menu, the restaurant can make more of a profit.

3-4c | Writing Coherent Paragraphs

Directions: *Work a partner or partners and fill in the following blanks with complete sentences to develop a coherent paragraph. The* **topic** *of the paragraph is provided and transitions have been inserted.*

1. **Topic:** Restrictions on Fireworks Displays near Gas Stations

   a. To begin with, _____.

   b. However, _____.

   c. In fact, _____.

   d. Still, _____.

   e. Therefore, _____.

2. **Topic:** Online Stores vs. Brick-and-Mortar Stores

   a. Initially, _____.

   b. _____; anyway, _____.

   c. To put it briefly, _____.

   d. By the way, _____.

   e. All in all, _____.

3. **Topic:** How to Change a Tire

   a. First, _____.

   b. Then, _____.

   c. _____; next, _____.

   d. At this point, _____.

   e. Finally, _____.

4. **Topic:** Renewable Energy Sources

   a. To summarize, _____.

   b. With this in mind, _____.

   c. Unless, _____.

   d. _____; for this reason, _____.

   e. In other words, _____.

4-1 | Varying Sentence Structure

Review

Vary your sentence structures.

Don't use all short, simple sentences. Vary your sentence length, patterns, and rhythms to create different effects on readers. Read your sentences aloud to check for variety.

Combine sentences using conjunctions or transitions.

If you use a lot of short simple sentences, your writing will sound choppy. Try combining short sentences with the same subject, and use conjunctions to show the relationship between the ideas. You can also add extra details to make your sentences even more interesting and informative.

> Examples of short **simple sentences**: George Washington learned surveying. George Washington became a county surveyor.

> Example of **combined sentence**: George Washington learned surveying as a boy and became a county surveyor at 18.

Try combining short sentences with different subjects into compound sentences using coordinating conjunctions, such as *and, but, or,* or *so.*

> Example of a **compound sentence**: Upon Augustine Washington's death, his oldest son, Lawrence, inherited his largest estate, <u>and</u> his youngest son, George, inherited his smallest plantation.

You can also combine them into complex sentences using a subordinating conjunction, such as *although, because, until, when,* and *where.*

> Example of a **complex sentence**: When George Washington was just 20 years old, he inherited the Mount Vernon estate from his older brother.

If you use certain transitions, such as *as a result, however,* and *nevertheless,* to combine closely related ideas, you will need to use a semicolon before the transition. Notice that the transition connects two in complete sentence structures.

> Example of ideas combined with a **semicolon and transition**: Lawrence left Mount Vernon to his daughter; however, she died soon afterward, and the estate was passed to George.

Combine sentences using participial constructions.

Another way of combining sentences is to use a present participle (an *-ing* verb form) or a past participle (an *-ed* verb form). To do this, reduce one sentence to just a participial phrase; then add it to the other sentence. Remember that the subject of the sentence must also be the subject of the participle.

> Example of ideas combined with a **present participle**: <u>Hoping</u> for advancement in the British army, Washington learned all he could from his commanders.

> Example of ideas combined with a **past participle**: <u>Selected</u> by the Second Continental Congress to lead colonial troops, Washington became commander-in-chief of the Continental Army.

4-1a	Varying Sentence Structure

Directions: *Revise the paragraphs below. Use a variety of sentence types (simple, compound, complex, and compound-complex) in your revisions. Write the new paragraph in the area provided.*

1. Technological advances made it possible for people to illegally release movies and music over the Internet. There were little to no regulations for this type of piracy. Billions of dollars in revenue were lost annually. Many people lost jobs. These jobs have not come back. Legislation had to be passed to address the issue. The problem still exists. Laws have been instituted to combat this type of piracy.

    _____

    _____

    _____

2. International students face many challenges. They come to the United States. Some of the challenges are expected. Others are not as predictable. The world has become a much smaller place over the last decade. Cultures that were once totally isolated from the West now are able to peer into American culture from afar. This allows others access to a voyeuristic examination of America's social structure. It gives foreigners a once-rare opportunity to see the United States clearly. Issues arise for the fortunate few who travel to America in search of intellectual and personal pursuits. It can be said that international students face many academic and social challenges.

    _____

    _____

    _____

3. I met DJ Screw in 1998 through mutual acquaintances. He asked if I could assist his younger cousin with college applications. I promptly aided the young man. DJ Screw and I developed a friendship. I became the executive editor of a national rap magazine. I asked if he would like to write a feature column for the periodical. He agreed. I interviewed DJ Screw. I recorded our conservation. DJ Screw and I recorded a song. The song was his last.

    _____

    _____

    _____

4-1b   Varying Sentence Structure

Directions: *Use the topics below to develop paragraphs that expand the ideas; use a variety of sentence types. Use the indicated number of sentence types in each paragraph.*

1. **Topic:** Gun Control **(1 Simple Sentence/ 2 Complex Sentences/ 1 Compound Sentence/ 1 Compound-Complex Sentence)**

   _____

   _____

   _____

2. **Topic:** Conservation **(2 Compound Sentences / 2 Simple Sentences / 1 Complex Sentence)**

   _____

   _____

   _____

3. **Topic:** Cell Phone Use in Schools **(2 Simple Sentences / 1 Complex Sentence / 2 Compound Sentences)**

   _____

   _____

   _____

4. **Topic:** Global Warming **(1 Compound Sentence / 1 Simple Sentence / 1 Complex Sentence / 2 Compound-Complex Sentences)**

   _____

   _____

   _____

5. **Topic:** White Lies **(1 Simple Sentence / 3 Complex Sentences/ 1 Compound-Complex Sentence)**

   _____

   _____

   _____

4-1c Varying Sentence Structure

Directions: *Work with a partner or partners and alternate writing different sentence types as indicated, on each topic below. Keep alternating until, for each topic, you have formed a five-sentence, coherent paragraph that contains various sentence types, lengths, and openings.*

I. Topic: Music Piracy

(1) _____ [Complex]

(2) _____ [Simple]

(3) _____ [Complex]

(4) _____ [Compound]

(5) _____ [Complex]

II. Topic: Protest through Social Media

(6) _____ [Compound-Complex]

(7) _____ [Complex]

(8) _____ [Simple]

(9) _____ [Complex]

(10) _____ [Simple]

III. Topic: Co-Parenting

(11) _____ [Simple]

(12) _____ [Compound]

(13) _____ [Complex]

(14) _____ [Compound]

(15) _____ [Complex]

IV. Topic: Dating in the Twenty-First Century

(16) _____ [Compound]

(17) _____ [Compound-Complex]

(18) _____ [Simple]

(19) _____ [Complex]

(20) _____ [Compound]

| **4-2** | Making Subjects and Verbs Agree |

Review

Make sure the subject and verb of your sentence agree.

In any sentence, the subject and verb must agree in number and person. **Number** refers to singular or plural. If there's just one, the subject is singular. If there are more than one, it's plural. For first person (*I*, *we*) and second person (*you*), there's no difference in the verb. But for third person (*he*, *she*, *it*, *they*), there is a difference. In general, a third person singular verb ends in -*s*, but a third person plural verb does not.

- Example of a **singular noun and verb**: My history <u>class meets</u> on Mondays and Thursdays.

- Examples of a **plural noun and verb**: <u>Classes begin</u> next week. <u>Geese are</u> very territorial.

If a prepositional phrase or dependent clause comes between the subject and verb, double-check to make sure the verb agrees with its subject.

Example of **agreement with a distant subject**: <u>One</u> of my classes <u>meets</u> in the auditorium.

Use plural verbs with compound subjects.

If two or more subjects are joined by *and*, they form a compound subject and take a plural verb.

Example of **agreement with a compound subject**: <u>Thunder and lightning frighten</u> my dog.

Make sure the verb agrees with the nearest alternative subject.

When subjects are joined by *or*, the verb agrees with the subject that's closest to it.

Examples of **agreement with an alternative subject**: Depending on the nature of the case, the judge or the <u>jurors determine</u> guilt. Depending on the nature of the case, the jurors or the <u>judge</u> determines guilt.

Determine whether a collective noun is singular or plural.

A collective noun refers to a group of people, animals, or things, such as *choir*, *swarm*, or *stack*. Collective nouns are considered singular when the emphasis is on the unit and are considered plural when the emphasis is on the individual elements. The verb is singular when the emphasis is on the unit and plural when it's on the individual elements.

- Example of **agreement with a singular collective noun**: On Sunday, the <u>choir is</u> performing Mozart's *Requiem*. (The choir is singing as a unit.)

- Example of **agreement with a plural collective noun**: The <u>swarm have</u> lost focus and begun to fly off in all directions.

4-2a   Making Subjects and Verbs Agree

Directions: *Rewrite the sentences to make the subjects and verbs agree.*

1. Michael and Mary runs a business together with their daughter who are a MBA.

   _____

2. The car dealership offers several discounts for veterans who works with inner-city programs.

   _____

3. Neither the coach nor the players wants to practice outside during the hot summer months.

   _____

4. Two are the most frequently used number in math problems.

   _____

5. Two hundred dollars are to be spent for the event, but the coordinator want to increase the budget.

   _____

6. Popcorn, candy, and soda is what most moviegoers buy before watching a long film at the theater.

   _____

7. The big dog need a large yard to run and plays.

   _____

8. Johnny work for a company that are in many states.

   _____

9. The concept of inertia are taught in some science classes at the community college.

   _____

10. Sanaa and Avah is really close relatives.

    _____

11. Kasen never argue or disagree with his dad, Eric, about his bedtime.

    _____

12. The hummingbird love to bathe in the birdbath that sit in the backyard.

    _____

4-2b   Making Subjects and Verbs Agree

Directions: *Underline the subject and verb errors in the paragraph below and rewrite the sentences to correct the problems.*

(1) The Biblical scheme of Michelangelo's Sistine Chapel ceiling clearly express the level of influence that religion play within High Renaissance social structure. (2) After being commissioned to paints the Sistine Chapel, Michelangelo embarks on a process to capture the very essence of mankind in a series of paintings. (3) As the basis for the work, Michelangelo choose man's salvation. (4) Of course, in accordance with the dominant doctrine of the period, salvation are offered to all through Jesus' sacrifice via the church. (5) Simply stated, the Sistine Chapel painting show how God create the world for man. (6) Later, of course, man lose God's favor and receive mortality as the ultimate punishment. (7) However, God does provides man with hope for redemption through Jesus. (8) God, as indicated within the work, have prewritten man's history through Adam's lineage as a means to become one with the most high following the end of one's physical life on Earth. (9) In other words, Michelangelo's painting seem to define what it mean to be human. (10) Humanity during this historical period, are eternally intertwined with religion. (11) Although Michelangelo's work are religious in nature, it also imply a deeper examination of self. (12) A study of self, by its very nature, is an intellectual pursuit at the most essential level of comprehension and can acts as yet another window into the High Renaissance.

1. _____
2. _____
3. _____
4. _____
5. _____
6. _____
7. _____
8. _____
9. _____
10. _____
11. _____
12. _____

4-2c | Making Subjects and Verbs Agree

Directions: *Use the following topics and verbs to create sentences with correct subject-verb agreement.*

1. _____[Either the boys or the coach/ watch or watches]

2. _____[Dr. Cherry Gooden/ teach or teaches]

3. _____[Aakhansha and Megan/ talk or talks]

4. _____[The Houston Rockets team/ play or plays]

5. _____[Gerron and Britini/ love or loves]

6. _____[Dean Straus, Jacki, and Rachel/ laugh or laughs]

7. _____[Rebecca Goosen or Betty Fortune/ run or runs]

8. _____[The Sandfiers and the Mourads/ travel or travels]

9. _____[The police department/ hire or hires]

10. _____[Cell phone technology/ control or controls]

11. _____[Late-night TV programs/ show or shows]

4-3 | Revising Sentence Fragments

Review

Every sentence has a complete subject and a complete predicate. These are the subject and verb along with their modifiers. A sentence expresses a complete thought.

A **sentence fragment** may look like a sentence, but it doesn't express a complete thought.

Make sure each sentence has a subject and a predicate.

A fragment may be missing a subject or a predicate. If it's missing a subject, the reader knows what is being done, but not who or what is doing or experiencing it. If it's missing a predicate, the reader knows who or what is being talked about, but not what they're doing or experiencing. The sentence needs to include both types of information to express a complete thought.

> Example of a **fragment without a subject**: Raced toward the finish line. You can fix this by adding a subject: <u>The contestants</u> raced towards the finish line.

> Example of a **fragment without a predicate**: Every dog in the kennel—big or small, young or old. You can fix this by adding a predicate: Every dog in the kennel—big or small, young or old—<u>began barking at exactly 5:00 p.m</u>.

Make sure each sentence expresses a complete thought.

If a **participial phrase** (beginning with an *-ing* or *-ed* verb form) is written as a sentence, it doesn't express a complete thought. If you see this situation, find a complete sentence before or after it that tells you the actor and action involved and connect the two.

> Example of a **fragment (participial phrase)**: Confused by the busy intersection. This would be complete if joined with a sentence that completes the thought: Confused by the busy intersection, <u>the lost toddler began to cry</u>.

If a **dependent clause** is written as a separate sentence, it doesn't express a complete thought, even though it contains a subject and a verb. You can recognize a dependent clause because it may start with a subordinating conjunction, such as *because* or *although*, or with a relative pronoun such as *who* or *that*. Look nearby for an independent clause the dependent clause belongs with.

> Example of a **fragment (dependent clause)**: Because they have swarm intelligence. This would be complete if joined with an independent clause that completes the thought: Because they have swarm intelligence, <u>honeybees can effectively make collective decisions</u>.

Avoid separating an appositive from the rest of the sentence.

An **appositive** renames someone or something. It should be part of the sentence that contains the noun it renames.

> Example of a **fragment (appositive)**: The third president of the United States. This appositive must appear in the same sentence as the name it modifies: <u>Lewis and Clark were asked to find the Northwest Passage by Thomas Jefferson</u>, the third president of the United States.

| **4-3a** | Revising Sentence Fragments |

Directions: *Rewrite the fragments to create complete sentences.*

1. The problem she anticipates.

   _____

2. Although Melinda and Rick became good friends.

   _____

3. Following the team's loss, the captain.

   _____

4. The class has many students, but only.

   _____

5. His brother living in Chicago.

   _____

6. Even with the new changes.

   _____

7. From the start, the two boys and their grandmother only.

   _____

8. The famous football star and his team all.

   _____

9. Talking to the driver about the different routes to the game.

   _____

10. While sitting in the room waiting for the teacher to arrive.

    _____

11. In the area behind the garage where the cable box sits.

    _____

12. Before paying the entire amount for the carpet.

    _____

4-3b | Revising Sentence Fragments

Directions: *Rewrite the fragments to create complete sentences.*

1. Serbino Sandifer, the award-winning journalist who wrote many notable national articles.

   The award-winning journalist, Serbino Sandifer, has written many notable national articles.

2. The students in the class.

   The students in the class, really enjoyed their teacher.

3. Since he loves to write.

   Give Joey a pen and pad, since he loves to write

4. The two children who have loving grandparents from another country.

   The two children who have loving grandparents from another country, were often missed

5. Probably the most successful singer of all times.

   Ruth Brown is probably the most successful singer of all time.

6. From his favorite film of the last two years.

   Joey loved the acting from his favorite film of the last 2 years.

7. Traditional methods of learning to revise sentence fragments.

   Traditional methods of learning to revise sentence fragments often escape me.

8. Almost the entire team that was expected to play in the big game tomorrow.

   Almost the entire team that was expected to play in the big game tomorrow, called in sick

9. According to the most recent research in the field of nanotechnology.

   According to the most research in the field of nanotechnology predicts that we are doomed

10. To question the witness.

    The was an attempt to question the witness.

11. No longer the strong symbol of independence and prosperity.

    The United States is, no longer the strong symbol of independence and prosperity.

12. Smiling in the face of danger with no other options.

    It takes great resolve to smile in the face of danger with no options.

13. Most of the singers from Argentina and Brazil.

    Most of the singers from Argentina and Brazil have not been heard of in the main stream

4-3c Revising Sentence Fragments

Directions: *Read the following paragraphs. Working as a group, identify all fragments. Rewrite each fragment as a complete sentence to correct the sentence fragment problems.*

I. The author turns to a more personal experience. To lend credence to her original thesis. As an individual. Who did not have the fortune of today's technological comforts. When she attended college, her invisible umbilical cord to her parents was abruptly severed on her first day as a freshman on her college's campus. She explains how the expense of long-distance calls and often-burdensome trips inhibited her parents. From maintaining a high level of strict scrutiny over her social interactions. Thus, she subconsciously sought alternative. Means to acquire guidance through college years. This transference of admiration and mentorship. Led to discussion between her and her parents about the life-altering wisdom of instructors and advisors.

II. Cortez admitting to becoming something of a know-it-all during family conversations. In one noteworthy conversation. She states that her father's understanding. When she openly doubted his ability to truly comprehend. The gravity and complexity of the Gulf War surprised her. After their talk, she began to. Define her life, as a young formative thinker, not within the confines of the safe haven of what she thought of as home, but from a more mature perspective.

I. _____

_____

_____

_____

_____

_____

_____

II. _____

_____

_____

_____

_____

_____

_____

4-4 | Revising Run-On Sentences and Comma Splices

Review

Identify run-on sentences and comma splices.

A **run-on sentence** occurs when two or more independent clauses appear beside each other with no punctuation between them.

> Example of a **run-on sentence**: Perry is a newspaper editor my friend Jimmy works for him.

A **comma splice** is similar. Two independent clauses are placed beside each other with only a comma between them.

> Example of a **comma splice**: Jennifer plays violin beautifully, she auditioned for the city orchestra.

Create two separate sentences.

One way to fix a run-on sentence or a comma splice is to make the to clauses into two separate sentences. To do this, place a period between them, and start the second clause with a capital letter.

> Examples of **separate sentences**:

- Perry is a newspaper editor. My friend Jimmy works for him.
- Jennifer has studied violin for fifteen years. She decided to audition for the city orchestra.

Create a compound sentence.

Another way to fix a run-on sentence or a comma splice is to create a compound sentence. To do this, add a comma and a coordinating conjunction after the first clause.

> Examples of **compound sentences**:

- Perry is a newspaper editor, and my friend Jimmy works for him.
- Jennifer has studied violin for fifteen years, so she decided to audition for the city orchestra.

Create a complex sentence.

Yet another strategy for fixing a run-on sentence or comma splice is to create a **complex sentence**, using one independent and one dependent clause. To do this, introduce the dependent clause with a subordinating conjunction or a relative pronoun. If the dependent clause comes at the beginning of the sentence, place a comma between the clauses. If it comes at the end, don't use a comma.

> Examples of **complex sentences**:

- Because Jennifer has studied violin for fifteen years, she decided to audition for the city orchestra.
- My friend Jimmy works for Perry, who is a newspaper editor.

4-4a	Revising Run-On Sentences and Comma Splices

Directions: *Revise each sentence to correct the run-on and comma splice errors.*

1. Michael loves to sing Mary is his best friend.

   _____

2. The dogcatcher patrols this area at night, he normally picks up several strays at 2 a.m.

   _____

3. Zro is a native Houstonian he lives in Missouri City.

   _____

4. Television programs are more provocative today edgier material is now fairly common.

   _____

5. When the temperature drops, fewer insects come out roaches never die though.

   _____

6. The Museum District is an expensive area to live, mostly doctors live there in mansions.

   _____

7. Few people use pagers doctors on call are probably the last major group to still use them.

   _____

8. What happened to the bonuses where did all the profits go?

   _____

9. Running with bulls is a dangerous practice it is a large part of their culture.

   _____

10. Holidays vary among countries Christmas is one the few universal ones celebrated.

    _____

11. Fresh drinking water is a global issue how can Americans use it to flush toilets?

    _____

12. Annie drives a Toyota truck, Anjana drives a Toyota sedan.

    _____

4-4b | Revising Run-On Sentences and Comma Splices

Directions: *Revise each sentence to correct the run-on and comma splice errors.*

1. The professor gives several tests students think that they are too difficult.

   The professor gives several test. Students think they are too dificult

2. Of the four men, three are brothers Michael is the oldest.

   Michael is the oldest of the 4 brothers.

3. The dog barks all night, neighbors constantly complain about the noise.

   Neighbors constantly complain about the noise of the barking dog all night

4. What department do you work for how did you become a supervisor?

   How did you become the supervisor of the department you work for. what department are you in?

5. The zoo opens at 10 a.m., the polar bear exhibit is closed for repairs.

   The zoo opens at 10AM. Too bad the polar bear exhibit is closed for repairs.

6. Indigenous people are sometimes displaced by modernization their way of life is destroyed.

   When indigenous people are displaced by modernization, their way of life is destroyed

7. What are your long-term goals, try to make your goals align with your current career trajectory.

   What are your long-term goals? Try to make your goals align with your current career.

8. The baker does not work on Saturdays, his employees work on weekends.

   The baker does not work on Saturdays. His employees work on weekends.

9. P.E. is an important class nevertheless, schools are cutting P.E. programs to save money.

   Even though P.E. is an important class, schools are cutting those programs to save money.

10. Virtual Reality is a great new technology it has lots of potential as a tool for learning.

    Virtual Reality, a great new technology, has lots of potential as a tool for learning

11. Time is a human-made construct of thinking, there are a number of theories on time measurement.

    Time is a human-made construct of thinking. There are a number of theories on time measurement.

12. CrossFit has become the hot new trend for millennials older people are not as engaged.

    CrossFit has become the hot new trend for millennials. Older people are not as engaged as the younger generation.

4-4c Revising Run-On Sentences and Comma Splices

Directions: *With a partner or partners, rewrite each sentence to correct the run-on and comma splice errors as indicated.*

1. Kasen loves to watch PJ Mask, he also like dinosaurs.

    _____ [2 Independent Clauses]

    _____ [Coordinating Conjunction]

    _____ [Subordinating Conjunction]

    _____ [Semicolon]

2. The hairdresser always overcharges his clients he charges additional fees for small things.

    _____ [2 Independent Clauses]

    _____ [Coordinating Conjunction]

    _____ [Subordinating Conjunction]

    _____ [Semicolon]

3. Damien and Davien are twins, Eric and Erris are not twins but they are all brothers.

    _____ [2 Independent Clauses]

    _____ [Coordinating Conjunction]

    _____ [Subordinating Conjunction]

    _____ [Semiolon]

4. Several hunters swear that they have seen Bigfoot it may be an undiscovered American primate.

    _____ [2 Independent Clauses]

    _____ [Coordinating Conjunction]

    _____ [Subordinating Conjunction]

    _____ [Semicolon]

5-1 | Choosing Appropriate Language

Review

It's important to address your readers with respect and use a level of formality they expect from college-level writing.

Use formal language.

Avoid slang, colloquialisms, and vulgar language. *Slang* is informal language that is not considered standard English. *Colloquialisms* are expressions used in certain regions but not throughout the country. Rather than using a slang term or a colloquialism, look for a standard English term that is familiar to a wider audience. (Of course, if you are writing dialogue, you might use slang and colloquialisms to make your writing authentic.) *Vulgar language* is offensive language. It includes profanity, crude body references, and other obscene language. As you write, be aware of how your words might affect others.

> Examples of using **formal language**:
>
> - Instead of describing someone as "extra," you might describe that person as "dramatic" or their behavior as "excessive."

Use bias–free language.

Writers should use language free of bias to ensure fair treatment of groups and individuals. Avoid use of any language that demeans or discriminates, and strive to use accurate, inclusive language at all times. To do this, describe people and groups with an appropriate level of specificity and be sensitive to labels. See the APA website (apastyle.apa.org) for more guidance and examples.

> Example of using **bias–free language**:
>
> - Instead of explaining that an experimental group consists of those "with intellectual disabilities," you might explain that an experimental group consists of those "diagnosed with dyslexia and dysgraphia."

Use clear, precise language.

Avoid using clichés. *Clichés* are words and phrases that have been so overused that they've lost their meaning. They may once have been fresh and impactful, but that is no longer true. Using clichés may give the impression your essay lacks original thought.

> Examples of **clear, precise language**:
>
> - Instead of using the phrase "heart of gold," use "generous" or "compassionate."

5-1a	Choosing Appropriate Language

Directions: *Rewrite the following sentences to improve clarity by using a thesaurus and dictionary to find more appropriate language to express the intended idea of the underlined passage. Consider the implied meaning of the underlined words. In your revisions, choose language that emphasizes the meaning as the Intended Purpose of Statement directs.*

1. Intended Purpose of Statement: To express strong disagreement

    Employees <u>do not want</u> to work 60 hours per week.

    _____

2. Intended Purpose of Statement: To express a lack of enthusiasm

    The new menu <u>is not very popular</u> with frequent customers.

    _____

3. Intended Purpose of Statement: To express startling unawareness

    Scootie <u>did not know</u> that he had a test today.

    _____

4. Intended Purpose of Statement: To express deep regret

    The boy <u>felt bad</u> after stealing the piece of candy from the store.

    _____

5. Intended Purpose of Statement: To express extreme excitement

    Both children <u>were happy</u> when their father announced the family vacation plans.

    _____

6. Intended Purpose of Statement: To express a sense of loss

    Margaret <u>was sad</u> after her dog ran away.

    _____

7. Intended Purpose of Statement: To express despair

    He <u>did not know what to do</u> after being fired and being left by his wife.

    _____

8. Intended Purpose of Statement: To express optimism

    Kevin <u>believes that he will become</u> a better athlete.

    _____

5-1b   Choosing Appropriate Language

Directions: *Using the information provided, circle the level of formality needed for each sentence's Intended Statement of Purpose. Revise the sentences using language that better reflects the intended purpose.*

1. Level of formality of language: FORMAL   INFORMAL

    Intended Purpose of Statement/Context: External Memo from Corporation

    All of ya'll need to show up to work right after the crack of dawn unless you want to broke for the meeting.

    _____

2. Level of formality of language: FORMAL   INFORMAL

    Intended Purpose of Statement/Context: Personal Diary Entry

    The projected ramifications of the analysis indicate a fiscal shortfall of millions for next year's budget.

    _____

3. Level of formality of language: FORMAL   INFORMAL

    Intended Purpose of Statement/Context: Expository Essay Draft in Required Course

    Fool! Teen drinking is really, really, really a big ol' problem cuz many bad things happen in the end.

    _____

4. Level of formality of language: FORMAL   INFORMAL

    Intended Purpose of Statement/Context: Post on Social Media as Required by Your Job as a Recruiter

    At this spot, you can get lots of dough, so swing by and hit me up for the real deal.

    _____

5. Level of formality of language: FORMAL   INFORMAL

    Intended Purpose of Statement/Context: Application for a Position as a Medical Doctor

    I want to get a good job being a doctor at a rich person's hospital.

    _____

5-1c	Choosing Appropriate Language

Directions: *Working in pairs, decide on the appropriateness of the language used in each of the following sentences.*

Optional: *Correct any errors in inappropriate language in the blanks that follow each sentence.*

1. Stated to a manager at your job: Appropriate   Inappropriate

   "What's up, man? Do we have anything important to do? If not, I'm out."

   _____

2. Stated to your chemistry professor: Appropriate   Inappropriate

   "Man! This class sucks. I really don't get the periodic table at all."

   _____

3. Stated to a casual acquaintance: Appropriate   Inappropriate

   "Hey, friend! How're you feeling now that your husband's left you with no money?"

   _____

4. Stated to a group of English majors: Appropriate   Inappropriate

   "What is the theme of the short story? Please take into account the role of protagonist."

   _____

5. Stated to a customer at the restaurant where you were recently hired:

                                                                Appropriate   Inappropriate

   "Everything is good here. However, that's just what they told me to say."

   _____

6. Stated to a person whose parent has recently passed: Appropriate   Inappropriate

   "Don't cry. You'll see your dad again soon, at the rate you're eating and drinking."

   _____

7. Stated to a police officer who pulls you over: Appropriate   Inappropriate

   "I am aware that I was speeding, but my wife is in labor."

   _____

8. Stated to a patient in your medical practice: Appropriate   Inappropriate

   "What in the world have you been doing to your body? You look like a sack of potatoes."

   _____

5-2 | Using Concise Language

Review

Concise language is brief and to the point. Wordy sentences make it hard for readers to find the meaning. Revise your writing to make sure it's concise.

Eliminate redundant words or phrases.

A word is **redundant** if it repeats what other words say. Too much repetition and too many words can obscure meaning and bore readers. Check for and delete words and phrases that merely repeat what you have already said.

> Examples of cutting **redundant language**: ~~actual~~ fact, all ~~of~~ the soldiers, biography ~~of someone's life~~, merge ~~together~~, postpone ~~until later~~, write ~~down~~

Eliminate empty phrases.

Check for and delete words and phrases that add no meaning to your text. This will make your writing stronger and more direct.

> Examples of **empty phrases**: <u>At that point in time,</u> <u>the majority of</u> computers were found only in large corporations <u>as a consequence of</u> their size and cost.

> Revision: <u>Then,</u> <u>most</u> computers were found only in large corporations <u>due to</u> their size and cost.

Prefer the active voice.

If you know who did the action, you probably don't need to use **passive voice**. The **active voice** is often more direct and concise.

> Example of **passive voice**: The eclipse was looked forward to by everyone on the hilltop.

> Revision in **active voice**: Everyone on the hilltop looked forward to the eclipse.

Combine closely related sentences.

If two sentences are closely related, combining them can eliminate repeated words and phrases. This will make your writing clearer and more concise.

> Example of **closely related sentences**: To authenticate you, our system uses session cookies. To allow authentication and proper use of our service, you must enable session cookies.

> Revision: You must enable session cookies to allow authentication and enjoy full use of our system.

| **5-2a** | Using Concise Language |

Directions: *Rewrite the following sentences to improve their conciseness.*

1. Harriet, the woman who lives next to the green house where no child goes because it looks too scary due to its state of disrepair, wants to move back to her hometown of Vicksburg.

   _____

   _____

2. In the beginning of the school year, the overly ambitious and unrealistic expectations for academic achievement for the coming year are at their highest point of projection.

   _____

   _____

3. The old, dusty computer that sits in the corner next to the dilapidated, ragged, food-stained chair with the front left wobbly leg is newer than it appears.

   _____

   _____

4. Energetic and active dogs are usually animated and peppy as they spiritedly bounce from end to end of the expanse located at the rear fenced-in yard on the lawn outside the home.

   _____

   _____

5. The medical doctor, who practices medicine, is a physician who works in the field of treating sick people in a building that houses and treats those with infirmities.

   _____

   _____

6. The vintage, classic automobile is a car that operates like a horseless carriage that uses unleaded fuel.

   _____

   _____

7. Detectives are police officers who work as specialized employees of police departments who investigate cases by attempting to detect and explore clues, which are traces left by perpetrators.

   _____

   _____

5-2b | Using Concise Language

Directions: *Underline the parts of the paragraph that are wordy. Rewrite the paragraph to reduce redundancy.*

Teaching Philosophy

The ultimate goal of my teaching is to encourage excellence in achievement through teaching students, which is my purpose for being an instructor. Being an educator at institutions of higher learning for more than two decades, my mission, for more than twenty years, remains the same as professor. I work to help students who are underrepresented in higher education to become independent learners to be able to learn without the help of anyone else. I wholeheartedly believe that with my entire heart that to educate, one must focus on educating and teaching the whole person. Thus, my teaching philosophy reflects my core instructional belief is a desire to aid students in their efforts to take control of their respective academic trajectories through active participation and engagement. To accomplish this goal, I have developed and use a variety of instructional techniques that are aimed to engage students.

_____

_____

_____

_____

_____

_____

| **5-2c** | Using Concise Language |

Directions: *Work in pairs, rewrite the following sentences to be more concise.*

1. Students, those from other states, are charged out-of-state tuition because they are not from this state.

   _____

   _____

2. Throughout the film, the actor kept saying different jokes from the beginning of the movie to the end of the movie.

   _____

   _____

3. Although marijuana is legal in some states, it is still illegal and not allowable by law by the federal government.

   _____

   _____

4. While working as a cook in a restaurant, he became a father at the same time he worked as a chef who has a child.

   _____

   _____

5. The debt that she has accrued is a lot of money that she owes him from credit he extended to her that must be paid back.

   _____

   _____

6. Aakhanksha lives with her mom and dad, who are her parents from India, Suren and Anjana.

   _____

   _____

7. Dr. B. Richards is from Houston, which is in the state of Texas located in the United States.

   _____

   _____

5-3	Understanding Sound Alike and Look Alike Words

Review

Use sound-alike words correctly.

Homonyms are words that sound the same but have different meanings They're also spelled differently.

Sometimes, homonyms can mean very different things, so it's important not to mix them up.

> Example of **homonyms**: hole/whole
> - *Hole* refers to an empty area within a larger substance, as in "There's a <u>hole</u> in the bucket, so it won't hold water."
> - *Whole* means complete, or entire, as in "If I mend the bucket, it will be <u>whole</u> again."

Spell sound-alike words correctly.

To make sure you're conveying the meaning you intend, make sure you spell homonyms correctly. If you're not sure of the spelling, use a dictionary.

It's also a good idea to keep a list of words you misspell regularly. Use your list to double-check the spelling of homonyms in your essays. Remember that your computer's spellchecker won't catch misused words if they're spelled correctly.

> Examples of **commonly misused homonyms**:
>
> *there/their/they're*
>
> <u>There</u> are several ways for people to train <u>their</u> dogs. If <u>they're</u> lucky, the dogs will learn quickly.
>
> - *There* is a way of introducing a sentence. It can also mean the opposite of *here*. Notice that it's spelled like *here* but with a *-t* at the beginning.
> - *Their* is the third person possessive pronoun. To remember that *their* is spelled with an *-i*, you can remember that *I* is also a pronoun.
> - *They're* is a contraction of the pronoun *they* and the verb *are*. The apostrophe indicates that the *-a* is missing from *are*, and that this is a contraction.
>
> *affect/effect*
>
> Humidity <u>affects</u> the wood in your floors. What are the <u>effects</u> of high humidity? The wood swells, which may make your floors buckle.
>
> - In this sentence, *affect* is a verb meaning to influence, and *effect* is a noun meaning result. The two meanings are related.
> - You should be aware that *effect* can also be a verb. However, as a verb, it has a different meaning: to cause or achieve. Here's an example: My cousin ran for the council because he wanted to effect change in how the city is governed.
>
> *aid/aide*
>
> If you need <u>aid</u>, ask your <u>aide</u>. That's what aides are for.
> *Aid* means help and *aide* means someone who helps. *Aide* ends with an *-e* just like *someone*.

5-3a	Understanding Sound Alike and Look Alike Words

Directions: *Read the paragraph below and underline the sound-alike and look-alike words that are being misused. Rewrite the sentences using the correct words.*

Two improve my academic performance, I have eliminated all the factors that contributed to my current academic predicament. Specifically, I have sought assistance from older and more stable family members to lesson the economic burden placed upon me during previous semesters. This, in itself, has allowed a clearer perspective of my educational goals to develop. In addition, I now only work weekends and seldom except a work schedule of more than 20 ours per weak. Furthermore, I have signed up in the lab four help in all my academic areas. Mr. Lewis, Mrs. Tsui, and Mrs. Gala have all pledged there willingness to aid me in any manner I need to succeed and graduate. Although I must remain a member of the University band for scholarship purposes, I have otherwise limited my time dedicated to strictly band-based activities that are not routed in a course that I have enrolled inn. All in all, I will take any measures suggested too continue to further my education. Truthfully, I just do not have the financial means, nor do any of my immediate family members, to finance an education without financial aid. Thus, I humbly request, not a second chance, but one final opportunity to realize my potential.

1. _____

2. _____

3. _____

4. _____

5. _____

6. _____

7. _____

8. _____

9. _____

10. _____

5-3b   Understanding Sound Alike and Look Alike Words

Directions: *On a separate sheet of paper, write original sentences using the words provided. In the blanks, list words that sound or look like the provided words.*

1. affect: _____

2. mince: _____

3. lapse: _____

4. cession: _____

5. principal: _____

6. tract: _____

7. feat: _____

8. coarse: _____

9. tier: _____

10. chute: _____

| **5-3c** | Understanding Sound Alike and Look Alike Words |

Directions: *Identify the word or words being misused in each sentence. Rewrite the sentence using the correct word.*

1. The soldier's resilience really spoke to his medal during the war.

   _____

2. Mom always praise before we eat dinner or go on a trip.

   _____

3. There was a musky smell in the heir.

   _____

4. Mitchell did not have a job, so he did not qualify for the bank lone.

   _____

5. Every morning, the baker makes a fresh batch of roles for the lunch rush.

   _____

6. When I was in band, I played the symbol, which is not a popular instrument.

   _____

7. The five senses are cite, smell, taste, touch, and sound.

   _____

8. At school, the bully would teas Gary during recess.

   _____

9. At Yellowstone National Park, tourists often see eagles sore by, high in the sky.

   _____

10. Ever since his dog passed, he has been in a state of morning.

    _____

11. A person on a diet seldom orders desert when eating out.

    _____

12. The math teacher asked the class, "What's the axes on the graph?"

    _____

13. Smoking is band in most public areas.

    _____

5-3d | Understanding Sound Alike and Look Alike Words

Directions: *Divide into two groups. Fold this page in half vertically. DO NOT LOOK at the side that you are not assigned. Use a dictionary to look up the definitions of the words in your list. Write sentences using the wrong word. Exchange the list of sentences between the groups. Identify the inappropriate words and rewrite each sentence. Correct and discuss identified errors and rewritten sentences.*

	Specially	Especially			Pole	Poll
1.				1.		
	Though	Although			Envelope	Envelop
2.				2.		
	Quiet	Quite			Lose	Loose
3.				3.		
	Affect	Effect			Cord	Chord
4.				4.		
	Breathe	Breath			Pour	Pore
5.				5.		
	Lay	Lie			Desert	Dessert
6.				6.		
	Site	Cite			Its	It's
7.				7.		
	Advise	Advice			Passed	Past
8.				8.		
	Except	Accept			There	Their
9.				9.		
	Course	Coarse			Infer	Imply
10.				10.		
	Compliment	Complement			Fewer	Less

6-1 | Using Commas

Review

Commas are used to separate sections of a sentence. If you read a sentence aloud, you'll often notice that a comma is reflected in a pause that helps clump information that belongs together.

Use commas to separate compound clauses or items in a series.

Place a comma between two independent clauses before the coordinating conjunction. Place a comma after each item in a list—except the last one. Treat coordinate adjectives—more than one descriptive word modifying one noun—as items in a list.

- Example of **compound clauses**: Lincoln died, and Johnson became president.
- Example of **items in a series**: Citrus fruits include oranges, lemons, and limes.
- Example of **coordinate adjectives**: We heard the sounds of active, boisterous children.

Place a comma after an introductory word, phrase, or clause at the beginning of a sentence.

Introductory material includes prepositional and participial phrases, dependent clauses, interjections, and terms of address, among other things.

Examples of a **comma after introductory material**:

- After the meeting, the boss asked Salvatore to come to his office. (prepositional phrase)
- If the handle is loose, tighten the screw. (dependent clause)
- Ladies and gentlemen, the performance will begin shortly. (term of address)

Place commas around a word, phrase, or clause that interrupts the flow of sentence.

This includes prepositional and participial phrases, as well as nonessential information such as nondefining appositives and relative clauses.

Examples of **commas around interrupters**:

- The smith, sensing our approach, turned with his hammer still raised. (participial phrase)
- Cambridge University Press, which printed its first book in 1584, is the world's oldest publisher. (nondefining relative clause)

Use commas to separate dialogue from tag words or phrases.

Remember to place the comma inside the quotation marks whenever it follows the quoted material.

Example of a **quotation**: "People like us, who believe in physics," said Einstein, "know that the distinction between past, present, and future is only a stubbornly persistent illusion."

Use commas to organize dates, addresses, numbers, and titles.

- Example of a **date**: On Sunday, April 9, 1865, Lee surrendered.
- Example of a **number**: The population of Los Angeles in 2018 was 3,792,621.
- Example of an **address**: Rita Harris, 2792 San Felipe Road, Desert Hot Springs, CA

6-1a | Using Commas

Directions: *Rewrite each sentence, using or deleting commas as needed for correctness.*

1. I will graduate on May 10, 2020 from Capital State University.

    _____

2. From the beginning he seemed to be a very quiet person.

    _____

3. I have lived in Austin Texas, Laughlin, Nevada and Carson Wyoming.

    _____

4. According to the witness the suspect a man with short red hair carried a blue orange and pink bag with zippers.

    _____

5. Michael, and Doug are, very good friends from the middle school that is located in Redding Arizona.

    _____

6. Fermin Roman Jr. is a student who owns many cars, motorcycles, and boats.

    _____

7. Please meet me in New Orleans Louisiana in March, 2019.

    _____

8. Does she the woman in the blue dress always wear a hat with feathers and stripes?

    _____

9. Salma and Aziza's favorite colors are aqua and mauve and lime green is Monay's favorite color.

    _____

10. The teacher said "Where is the rest of the, class?"

    _____

11. The old lonely dog really misses his owner who died last week.

    _____

12. Can a person who has not finished college teach, any college courses?

    _____

6-1b   Using Commas

Directions: *Read the following paragraph. Circle the thirteen comma errors – commas that are either missing or misplaced – in the paragraph. in the blanks below, rewrite each sentence with a comma error to correct the mistake.*

---

(1) The article proceeds, by initially positing "All parents should afford their children an opportunity to grow, and learn independently to develop the social and academic skills they will need in adulthood." **(2)** This said the author allows for a more objective look at the phenomenon, by juxtaposing, her dual role as college administrator and parent. **(3)** As a parent she acknowledges the difficulty that one is likely to face, when asked to disregard his or her child's best interests, and allow the child to make life-altering decisions without interjecting. **(4)** Furthermore the work develops, to posit the notion that parental contact adversely affects, the social progress of a burgeoning adult. **(5)** In other words if parents do not allow their child, to make certain mistakes, the child's transition into adulthood and independence may be negatively impacted. **(6)** Therefore it is imperative to provide a child, with enough space to mature without feeling constrained by an irrational fear of failure or rejection.

---

1. _____

2. _____

3. _____

4. _____

5. _____

6. _____

6-1c | Using Commas

Directions: *Working in pairs, find the comma errors in the sentences below. Then, rewrite the sentences, correcting the errors.*

1. The funny rich man from the TV show is coming to our school tomorrow to speak.

    _____

2. William Engleson Jr. is the son of the banker who lives at 5656 Mulberry Street in New Town Texas.

    _____

3. If you go past the store please pick up some bread milk cookies-and-cream ice cream and batteries if they are on sale.

    _____

4. I do believe that they met on June 15 1987 at the old rickety amusement park.

    _____

5. The waiter, said "Our special today is alligator stew with garlic toast."

    _____

6. Will he the guy from her class really help me with work too?

    _____

7. I have lived in Las Vegas, Nevada for most of my adult life.

    _____

8. In the notes the professor since he thinks he is funny always includes a joke but not a very funny one.

    _____

9. If the car, does not start, again you should think about buying a newer, more reliable vehicle soon.

    _____

10. Books paper, and pens are required in most classes but some mostly younger instructors only use computers.

    _____

6-2	Using Capital Letters

Review

When writing for college, it is important to use capital letters in order to communicate clearly.

Begin each sentence with a capital letter.

Remember that a quotation may also be a sentence. If your sentence contains a quotation that is a complete sentence, use a capital letter to begin the quotation as well.

> Examples of **capital letters to begin sentences and quotes**:

- <u>T</u>he factory closed last year. <u>T</u>his year, it reopened as a shopping mall.
- <u>B</u>arrie's novel begins, "<u>A</u>ll children, except one, grow up."

Capitalize the main words in titles.

Don't capitalize articles (*a, an, the*), the infinitive *to*, prepositions (e.g., *to, from, with, by*), or coordinating conjunctions (e.g., *and, but, or, so*)—unless they are the first word in the title or the first word after a colon or dash.

> Examples of **capitalization in titles**:

- *War and Peace*
- "Taking the High Road: A Journey to the Edge of the World"
- *The Man in the High Castle*

Capitalize the pronoun *I* and all proper nouns and adjectives.

A proper noun is the name of someone or something and, unlike a common noun, needs to be capitalized, and so does an adjective created from a proper noun. If a common noun is part of name, it must also be capitalized.

> Example of a **capital *I***: When <u>I</u> fly, <u>I</u> prefer a window seat.

> Examples of **proper nouns**: Charles Dickens (person), Indonesia (place), Thursday (day of the week), Standard Oil (organization), British Museum (thing)
> Note that the words *oil* and *museum* are normally common nouns and not capitalized. Here, though, they are part of the company name.

> Examples of **proper adjectives**: Dickensian, Indonesian, African American

Capitalize a title before a person's name.

> Examples of **titles preceding names**: <u>Ms</u>. Sanchez, <u>President</u> Lincoln, <u>Prime Minister</u> Howard, <u>General</u> Grant, <u>Lady</u> Thatcher

However, if a title is not used before a name, it is not capitalized.

> Example of a **title not preceding a name**: Herbert Hoover was elected <u>president</u> in 1928.

6-2a | Using Capital Letters

Directions: *Underline all capitalization errors in the following sentences. Rewrite each sentence to correct the error.*

1. I have never attended robert johnson High School in alberta, New mexico.

   _____

2. my favorite season is Summer because winter is too cold.

   _____

3. although I really enjoy History 1301, I do not think my Professor knows who I am.

   _____

4. The man shouted, "stop doing all of that yelling!"

   _____

5. I was told to drive North along Brightwater road and make a left near red dog creek.

   _____

6. my wife loves the Ocean because it reminds her of her childhood in miami.

   _____

7. david is chinese; however, he speaks spanish fluently.

   _____

8. the most celebrated Holidays in my city are Christmas, thanksgiving, and Halloween.

   _____

9. The u.s. constitution is a very important Federal document that has relevance for all aspects of American life.

   _____

10. Someone, please call the Doctor!

    _____

11. Call Of The Wild is one of my favorite books to read for pleasure.

    _____

12. His Mother would buy him all name brands, such as nike, adidas, and Gucci, for his birthday.

    _____

6-2b | Using Capital Letters

Directions: *Read the below introduction from a persuasive speech outline. Underline each word that contains a capitalization error. Rewrite the sentences in the spaces provided below, correcting the errors.*

I.   **(1)** Would You drink a Soda if you knew that You would develop type II diabetes from it? **(2)** What about if You knew that your teeth would rot by the time You reached the tenth Grade? **(3)** Moreover, would You drink a bottle of Soda if You would develop serious Weight Issues that might cause Premature Death?

II. **(4)** My Speech today is on the proposed institution of more stringent Federal Laws regarding the access of Sugar Sweetened Beverages for at-risk groups.

III. **(5)** The Johnson foundation and various other Expert Investigators provide ample research to support My Proposal.

IV. **(6)** The Regular Consumption of Sugar-Sweetened Beverages (SSBs) has been directly linked to a wide variety of avoidable health-related issues.

---

1. _____

2. _____

3. _____

4. _____

5. _____

6. _____

6-2c	Using Capital Letters

Directions: *Working in pairs, review the following sentences and underline all capitalization errors. Then, take turns rewriting the sentences with the errors corrected.*

1. if the lonestar bar and grill is open, then We can eat there this Evening.

   _____

2. Dr. Hillard Williams ed several Universities across the midwest before he came back to texas.

   _____

3. Since the movie e.t. is about e.t.s, then it is possible that Aliens are real and visiting our Planet.

   _____

4. The ancient romans had many different Gods, including Jupiter and Juno.

   _____

5. along the Bank of the River lies an abandoned chevrolet with Custom Rims and ferrari kit.

   _____

6. Despite the sunshine, remember that hurricane Dave is still headed this way and should arrive Wednesday Night.

   _____

7. Did you order Chinese food from the china house restaurant that's in the asian shopping district?

   _____

8. Most High School principals do not have a phd in education like dr. Henry Tran does.

   _____

9. Annie tsui is from Texas, but her Husband steve is from hong kong.

   _____

10. german chocolate cake is not a german desert; It is an american desert.

    _____

11. As a child, i played pac-man every day after school at the Convenience store across from frost elementary.

    _____

| **7-1** | Understanding Plagiarism |

Review

Acknowledge the words and ideas of others.

Plagiarism is using someone else's words, ideas, photos, or other materials without letting your audience know they are not your own. If you submit a paper written by a friend, bought from a website, or copied from online sources, that's plagiarism. In college, plagiarizing can have serious consequences—from a failing grade to expulsion.

Unfortunately, careless research habits can lead to unintentional plagiarism. Just because materials are easily available online, it doesn't mean you are free to use them as your own.

Clearly differentiate others' words and ideas from your own.

This means using quotation marks around another person's exact words and supplying an in-text citation.

> Example of a **quotation**:
> As John Dewey (1916) observed, "The criterion of the value of school education is the extent in which it creates a desire for continued growth and supplies means for making the desire effective in fact."

But it is also plagiarism if you paraphrase someone else's ideas—that is, restate their ideas in your own words—but do not credit that person. That means you need to provide an in-text citation for a paraphrase as well.

> Example of a **paraphrase**:
> John Dewey (1916) noted that the benefit of schooling can be measured by how much it makes a student want to keep learning and how well it prepares them to do so.

Notice how the writer has used different words but kept the ideas and even the order in which Dewey wrote them.

Summarizing is stating someone else's ideas in a shorter form. When you summarize, you also need to provide an in-text citation.

> Example of a **summary**:
> You can judge a child's education by the adult's pursuit of knowledge (Dewey, 1916).

7-1a | Understanding Plagiarism

Directions: *Answer each of the below questions, and clearly explain your answers.*

1. What is plagiarism?

   _____

2. If a student reads a book and uses a quote from the book without referencing the author, is that considered plagiarism? If so, why?

   _____

3. If a student includes a graph in a paper but does not say where it comes from, is that plagiarism?

   _____

4. If you have a works-cited list, but you do not use in-text citations within your work, is that plagiarism?

   _____

5. If you combine your ideas with the ideas of an author but do not cite the author, is that plagiarism?

   _____

6. If a friend in your history class gives you her essay so that you can use it for your English class, is that plagiarism?

   _____

7. If you use a quote from a person, but you do not use quotation marks or cite the source, is that plagiarism?

   _____

8. Would the following statement be considered plagiarism? If so, why? Michael Jackson believed that everyone has an inner child who wants to explore.

   _____

9. Provide an example of plagiarism.

   _____

10. If a student includes quotation marks, but no citation, is that plagiarism?

   _____

7-1b | Understanding Plagiarism

Directions: *Determine whether the below situations describe instances of plagiarism; briefly explain your responses. Then, answer the question at the bottom of this page.*

Situation 1

Annie Tsui creates a PowerPoint presentation for her job. In the presentation, she includes data from nearby universities. However, she does not include any citations or a reference page.

Is this a case of plagiarism? Why or why not?

_____

Situation 2

James L. Robertson writes an essay for his psychology class. He uses the same paper for an assignment in his English class.

Is this a case of plagiarism? Why or why not?

_____

Situation 3

Montez Hines, a professor at your college, writes an article for an academic journal. When submitting the final version to the publication, she forgets to include her works-cited page. Because the journal has a strict deadline, it publishes Prof. Hines's article without the references, in its online format and its print volume.

Is this a case of plagiarism? Why or why not?

_____

Scenario 4

Darin loves to sing and write songs. For his friend's birthday, he writes a beautiful ballad and incorporates parts of the friend's favorite childhood songs into his ballad. Darin uses quotation marks around all lyrics from other songs and cites the sources.

Is this a case of plagiarism? Why or why not?

_____

What is the difference between plagiarism and paraphrasing?

_____

7-1c   Understanding Plagiarism

Directions: *Read each statement and, as a group, determine whether it describes plagiarism. Then, sort the statements in the blanks below.*

a) Using quotes and citing the source material

b) Using some words from a source mixed with your words

c) Using a direct quote without quotation marks but with citations

d) Copying information from a website

e) Reusing an old essay that you wrote for another class

f) Rewriting someone else's ideas in your words

g) Using a fictional source as a citation

h) Crediting an author whose work you have not used, even as background

i) Paraphrasing

j) Cutting and pasting from several sources to write

k) Using a friend's essay with her permission

l) Buying an essay, but adding your ideas and citations

m) Using a paragraph from an old essay in a new one

n) Using an outline your instructor provided to write a paper

o) Making a mistake in a citation

p) Hiring an editor and submit work without citing the editor

Plagiarism	*Both*	*Not Plagiarism*
_____	_____	_____
_____	_____	_____
_____	_____	_____
_____	_____	_____
_____	_____	_____
_____	_____	_____
_____	_____	_____
_____	_____	_____
_____	_____	_____
_____	_____	_____
_____	_____	_____
_____	_____	_____

| **7-2** | Knowing What and Why to Cite |

Review

Citing your sources tells readers your writing is accurate and well-informed. Cite your source when you quote a source's exact words, paraphrase content from a source, summarize content from a source, or use anything under copyright.

Cite sources of facts and expert opinions.

If you mention a **fact**, cite your source.

> Example of a **fact and citation**: The West African Ebola outbreak of 2014–2015 is believed to have begun when a bat infected a young child in Guinea (CDC, 2017).

Facts include specific numbers, statistics, and factual details.
If you state an author's opinion, cite your source.

> Example of an **opinion and citation**: According to the World Health Organization (2018), the global risk from the current outbreak is low.

Do not cite common knowledge.

If your reader can be expected to know the facts you're including, you don't need to cite them. They are considered **common knowledge**. Common knowledge includes dates, historic events, public documents, and well-known theories.

> Examples of **common knowledge**:

- George Washington was the first president of the United States.
- Sputnik I was launched on October 4, 1957.
- The first 10 amendments to the U.S. Constitution are referred to as the Bill of Rights.
- The second law of thermodynamics tells us that heat will naturally pass from a hotter object to a colder one—and not the other way around—until the two objects are at the same temperature.

However, if you gave information on these subjects that is less commonly known, you would need to cite your sources:

> Example of a less well-known **detail requiring citation**: General Washington estimated the number of Hessian mercenaries in Trenton to be about 1,500 (Washington, 1776).

Know your audience.

Of course, what is common knowledge can vary, depending on your audience. Think about what your readers already know about your subject. Consider their education level and occupation, both of which informs their level of knowledge.

7-2a | Knowing What and Why to Cite

Directions: *For each of the following categories, indicate whether the information should be cited. If it should be cited, briefly explain why.*

1. Information that is common knowledge

   Example: Houston is located in Texas.

   _____

2. Direct quote from a source.

   Example: Chad Lewis said, "I work at the Louis Vuitton store in the Galleria."

   _____

3. Paraphrase

   Example: The comet will return to Earth's orbit in twenty years.

   _____

4. Conclusion (following a passage that contains cited material)

   Example: Therefore, after reviewing the various theories, one concludes based on research that the universe is billions of years old.

   _____

5. Original research

   Example: I have learned that student persistence is directly correlated to retention rates.

   _____

6. Facts found in a source

   Example: As I read, I learned that the Great Wall of China can be seen from outer space.

   _____

7-2b	Knowing What and Why to Cite

Directions: *Fill in the blanks as specified with examples of information that must be cited; briefly explain why each citation is needed.*

<u>When</u>   <u>Why</u>

Quotation

_____   _____

_____   _____

Paraphrase

_____   _____

_____   _____

Summary

_____   _____

_____   _____

Fact

_____   _____

_____   _____

Statistic

_____   _____

_____   _____

Graph or Image

_____   _____

_____   _____

| **7-2c** | Knowing What and Why to Cite |

Directions: *Work with a partner or group to determine whether the situations listed below require citations; for those situations that do require citations, briefly explain why.*

Situation 1

An academic professional coauthors a document for publication in a scholarly journal.

Citation Required ☐   **Citation Not Required** ☐

_____

_____

Situation 2

Someone creates a document, idea, or presentation based on work from another source which uses indirect cites.

Citation Required ☐   **Citation Not Required** ☐

_____

_____

Situation 3

A content developer on a website uses an image she found on another website on her own.

Citation Required ☐   **Citation Not Required** ☐

_____

_____

Situation 4

A student introduces facts or information that comes from another source.

Citation Required ☐   **Citation Not Required** ☐

_____

_____

Situation 5

A writer paraphrases an article that uses an indirect source.

Citation Required ☐   **Citation Not Required** ☐

_____

_____

| **7-3** | Keeping Track of Sources |

Review

Save and organize your sources.

To avoid plagiarizing inadvertently, start keeping track of your sources as soon as you being researching your paper. If you're using Questia, you can use its citation tools to do so.

If you're using more than one library or database, you'll need to keep track of them on your computer. Set up a file and name it Research Materials. In it, save articles and lists of your sources, creating subfolders as needed.

> Example folder tree:

- Research Materials
  - o Australian geography
  - o Aboriginal tribes
  - o Dreamtime
  - o Legal battles

Keep a list of your sources.

As you find each source, put it on a list. Include all the information you will need for your Works Cited or References list: author, title, publisher, date, and if relevant, page range. Note that Questia will keep this list for you.

On your list, be sure to include links to web pages you use. Not only can you use this link to return to the page, but you will need to include the link in your Works Cited list. Keep a note, too, of each time you visit each web page.

Annotate your research materials.

Use Questia or the tools in the programs on your computer to mark up your saved documents and PDFs as well as web pages. Use the comment and sticky note tools to highlight useful facts and other details, and to make notes to yourself about how they relate to your topic or to another source.

If you see a quotation you might use in your paper, copy it, place it in quotation marks, and record its author, title, and page number. Remember to do this if you might paraphrase or summarize the material. This way, you can be sure you won't accidentally plagiarize it.

Refer to your notes as you write.

Use the notes you've taken to create in-text citations and a running Works Cited or References list as you work on your paper. That way, you know you won't forget to correctly document each detail and its source.

Questia and other online services will not only allow you to keep track of your sources but will also create your sources list. If you use one of these services, don't forget to check to make sure the list is complete and correctly formatted.

7-3a | Keeping Track of Sources

Directions: *Locate the sources listed below and fill in the blanks to document the sources. Please note the type of source required to answer each question is specified. Use the extra blank lines to add any additional information that is necessary to correctly document the source.*

1. Source: Scholarly Journal

   Author: _____

   Year of Publication: _____

   Title: _____

   Web Address: _____

   Publisher: _____

   _____

   _____

2. Source: Library Database

   Author: _____

   Year of Publication: _____

   Title: _____

   Web Address: _____

   City and State of Publication: _____

   Publisher: _____

   _____

   _____

3. Source: E-Book

   Author: _____

   Year of Publication: _____

   Title: _____

   Web Address: _____

   City and State of Publication: _____

   Publisher: _____

   _____

   _____

| **7-3b** | Keeping Track of Sources |

Directions: *Match the below sources with the correct category. Then, answer the questions that follow.*

a) "More Jobs in Tech to Come"

b) *Happy Times*

c) *Houston Chronicler*

d) Personal interview

e) *The Journal of Co-Requisite Design*

1. Book _____ Newspaper _____ Scholarly journal _____ Interview _____
   Article _____

2. What information would a works-cited entry for a webpage that is not an online newspaper, magazine, or journal need?

   _____

3. What information would a works-cited entry for an online periodical need that an entry for a print periodical would not need?

   _____

4. What information would a works-cited entry for a print book need that an entry for a print journal would not need?

   _____

5. Choose three different types of sources and fill in the below chart for each source. **(Note: All blanks are not needed for every source.)**

Author	Title	Pub. Date	Place of Pub.	Pub. Company	Vol. Num.	Page Num.	Company that posted webpage	Web Ad- dress	Date Retrieved

7-3c | Keeping Track of Sources

Directions: *With a partner or group, research online to find sources corresponding to the nine categories listed below; for each source, list the relevant information in the chart. If a column does not apply to a particular source, write an n/a in the column; if relevant information is not provided, write x in the column.*

Book   Interview
Article without author   Dissertation
Journal article   Encyclopedia
Website   Magazine
Online journal

Author	Title	Pub. date	Place of pub.	Name of Publisher	Vol. no.	Page nos.	Company that posted webpage	Web address (URL)	Date retrieved

| **7-4** | Using Copyrighted Materials Fairly |

Review

Copyrighted material is someone else's intellectual property. Most materials you will use in your academic assignments will be copyrighted material.

Cite the copyrighted material you use in your academic assignments.

Citing your source acknowledges that the material is not you own and gives credit to its creator. If you won't be publishing your paper, citing your source is enough.

Examples of copyrighted material:

- photographs and videos
- music and other sound files
- graphs, diagrams, and other images
- complete texts, such as magazine articles, poems, and short stories

Get permission to use copyrighted materials if you will be publishing your work.

Published work includes articles in the campus newspaper, a department magazine, or online.

There are two types of publication: for educational purposes and for commercial purposes. If your purpose is educational, you need fewer permissions than if it is commercial. But if it is commercial—if you intend to make money through your publication—getting permission can be more difficult and will be more expensive.

Whatever your purpose, if you are going to publish your writing, you need permission from the copyright holders to use their work. If you want to use a piece of music, a video, or a photograph, contact the copyright holders and ask to use it. Be especially careful if you want to post your work online.

Get written permission from the copyright holders. When you contact them, include the following:

- the purpose of your work—educational or commercial
- a description of how you intend to use the material
- a copy of your work (if possible)
- a link to the website where you intend to publish (if relevant)
- the name of the periodical or book in which you intend to publish (if relevant)

Note that if a written work is in copyright and you want to use it in a published piece, you can quote up to fifteen words without permission but must still cite the source. If you want to use more than fifteen words, contact the author and get permission. This includes song lyrics.

Be especially careful if you will be publishing your work online. Many websites publish images or other copyrighted materials without getting permission, but if you don't get permission, you are breaking the law.

| **7-4a** | Using Copyrighted Materials Fairly |

Directions: *Determine whether each of the following situations describes a fair use of copyrighted materials. If it is not fair use, please briefly explain how the copyrighted material can be used fairly.*

1. Using material for entertainment   Fair Use ☐   Not Fair Use ☐

2. Using material for teaching   Fair Use ☐   Not Fair Use ☐

3. Using material for published work   Fair Use ☐   Not Fair Use ☐

4. Using an entire work   Fair Use ☐   Not Fair Use ☐

5. Using material for a news report   Fair Use ☐   Not Fair Use ☐

6. Using material for distribution   Fair Use ☐   Not Fair Use ☐

7. Using material for nonprofit   Fair Use ☐   Not Fair Use ☐

8. Using material for research   Fair Use ☐   Not Fair Use ☐

9. Using a short passage of material   Fair Use ☐   Not Fair Use ☐

10. Using material for one-time use   Fair Use ☐   Not Fair Use ☐

7-4b	Using Copyrighted Materials Fairly

Directions: *Answer each of the following questions in complete sentences.*

1. What is the purpose of copyright?

_____

2. Kasen reads Flannery O'Connor's "A Good Man Is Hard to Find" and writes an article about the short story that is published in his school's newspaper. Which of the below situations is fair use of copyrighted material? Explain briefly.

   a. Kasen writes an opinion piece that uses only the title but does not make any specific references to the story.

   _____

   b. Kasen writes in-depth analysis of "A Good Man Is Hard to Find" that discusses the story as a literary masterpiece.

   _____

   c. Kasen copies the entire short story and submits it as an original work for the newspaper's fiction contest.

   _____

Are the following situations fair use of copyrighted material? Briefly explain why or why not.

3. Theodore works as an online blogger. In his most recent blog entry, he used copyrighted material as part of a slogan, as part of a negative campaign against a competing blog site.

   _____

4. Carlos includes copyrighted material in his scholarship essay.

   _____

5. While working at a movie studio, Salaam finds an unpublished script for an upcoming Marvel film. Salaam, a fan and comics enthusiast, makes thousands of copies and sells them at comic book conventions.

   _____

6. Ruthie works as a literary critic. She reviews Stephen King's newest novel by Stephen King, writing a scathing criticism that references many characters and settings in the work.

   _____

<table>
<tr><td>**7-4c**</td><td>Using Copyrighted Materials Fairly</td></tr>
</table>

Directions: *With a partner or group, conduct online research to find fair use and not fair use examples of each category listed below*

Fair Use

Research

_____

Criticism

_____

Parody

_____

News

_____

Nonprofit educational

_____

Educational

_____

Not Fair Use

Entertainment

_____

Commercial

_____

For-profit endeavor

_____

No copyright acknowledgment

_____

| **7-5** | Checking Source Use While Revising |

Review

It's important to accurate while taking research notes and just as important to be careful about your research after drafting your paper.

Check that you haven't plagiarized unintentionally.

Examine each sentence for facts and details that may have come from your sources. Make sure there's an in-text citation for each one. If you see a fact or detail that isn't common knowledge, you must cite its source. If it isn't, check your research to find the source, and add the in-text citation.

Look for quotations that are missing quotation marks. To do this, pay attention to the language you used. If there's a sudden shift in the style of the language, it may indicate that you've use a quotation without realizing it.

> Example of an **unmarked quotation**: Having an absentee father leads Huckleberry to suffer in unforeseen ways. For example, when Tom is setting up a pirate gang with his friends, the boys are about to take a blood oath. <u>They was going to rule me out</u>, Huck realizes, <u>because they said every boy must have a family or somebody to kill, or else it wouldn't be fair and square for the others.</u> Huck thinks quickly and offers the Widow's odious sister, Miss Watson, as a stand-in for his father.

If you find an unmarked quotation, check your notes to see where you got it. Then, place quotation marks around the quoted material, and add an in-text citation.

Check your paper against your sources.

Find each in-text citation and compare the source with what you've written. Did you get the fact or detail right? Is the quotation accurate? If you paraphrased, did you use your own words? If you summarized, is your summary accurate and in your own words?

Cross-reference your in-text citations with your bibliography.

Every in-text citation in your paper should correspond to an entry in your bibliography. Put your paper and your bibliography side by side and compare them. Find the bibliography entry that matches each in-text citation. If you find an in-text citation that doesn't match one of the bibliography entries, check your notes and create the bibliography entry.

There are many different citation styles. The two most common are MLA and APA. In MLA, the bibliography is called Works Cited; in APA, it's called References. Whether it's called Works Cited or References, this type of bibliography lists only sources that have been cited in the paper.

Check to make sure that each of the sources mentioned in your reference list is cited in the paper. If you have an entry in the reference list that doesn't correspond to at least one in-text citation in the paper, remove that entry.

| **7-5a** | Checking Source Use While Revising |

Directions: *Read the following passage and check sources for correct APA citation format. Note the formatting errors and correct them in the spaces below (you may need to invent data if missing from citation).*

The work summarizes the latest developments about physical fitness and several health outcomes in young people. (1) The literature suggests that cardiorespiratory fitness levels are associated with total and abdominal adiposity **(Gonzales)**. (2) It also states that both cardiorespiratory and muscular fitness are shown to be associated with established and emerging cardiovascular disease risk factors **(1999, Michaels & Johnson)**.

(3) In addition, the work directly implies improvements in muscular fitness and speed/agility, rather than cardiorespiratory fitness, seem to have a positive effect on skeletal health **(2002, p.67, Chen)**. (4) To this end, both cardiorespiratory and muscular fitness enhancements are recommended in pediatric cancer patients/survivors in order to attenuate fatigue and improve their quality of life **(1978, Kazinsky)**.

(5) After extensive research, it can also be said that improvements in cardiorespiratory fitness have positive effects on depression, anxiety, mood status and self-esteem **(2010 Williams: Singh and Krieg, 2009)**. Furthermore, it seems to be associated with a higher academic performance. This assertion alone acts as a good argument to maintain physical fitness programs in schools.

1. _____

2. _____

3. _____

4. _____

5. _____

7-5b   Checking Source Use While Revising

Directions: *For each of the below situations, determine the source(s) being used, then state whether the source described is credible. If it is not, then provide a credible alternative in the space provided.*

1. For Oscar Jones' Business 101 essay, he uses information that one of his friends, a fellow undergraduate student who is a video gaming expert, verbally tells him. Oscar cites his friend's comments as a personal interview; he uses the comments to support his analysis of the gaming industry.

    _____

    _____

2. George Carter is writing a report for his economics class; he uses information from a website whose organization is no longer certified. Although there is no way to verify the organization's information, George nevertheless includes the data as a major element of his report.

    _____

    _____

3. Amanda McCafferty drafts a proposal for writing her new book. As a part of the proposal, she includes a reference sheet in MLA and APA formats for verification of all sources of her research from scholarly journals.

    _____

    _____

4. For a group presentation assignment, Prof. Cherry Gooden requires students to use scholarly sources. However, Raphael, one of her students, conducts basic research online: he compiles information from .coms that are sponsored by companies that provide bias information rather than using the suggested .edu or .gov sites that Dr. Gooden pointed out to the class.

    _____

    _____

5. Herman Fisher has written a 20-page research paper. However, while editing it, he discovers that he has lost his notes on sources. In desperation, he makes up several citations and then uses different fictitious in-text citations.

    _____

    _____

7-5c	Checking Source Use While Revising

Directions: *With a partner or a group, read the following sources and statements, and determine whether they are credible. If they are not, please briefly explain, then discuss with a partner or group how to find a credible source to provide the indicated information.*

1. Source: Basic Internet search   Credible _____   Not Credible _____

   "The newest branch of the military is called Space Force."

   _____

2. Source: Science textbook   Credible _____   Not Credible _____

   "Water freezes at 32 degrees Celsius."

   _____

3. Source: A conversation with an expert   Credible _____   Not Credible _____

   "The budget deficit for the next fiscal year has long-term implications for new hires and market growth indicators."

   _____

4. Source: A scholarly journal   Credible _____   Not Credible _____

   "Transformational leadership is an emerging practice in higher education that offers promising results for institutions in dire need of change."

   _____

5. Source: A popular blog site   Credible _____   Not Credible _____

   "All the money from state lotteries is used to buy books for schools."

   _____

6. Source: A source cited in another published work   Credible _____   Not Credible _____

   "At its current rate of expansion, global warming will disrupt the earth's ecosystem to an extent that is irreversible within the next 20 to 25 years."

   _____

7. Source: A television commercial   Credible _____   Not Credible _____

   "Milk is the best source of calcium to help maintain healthy bones."

   _____

| **8-1** | Reading Critically |

Review

Reading critically means looking below the surface of what you're reading and really thinking about the ideas the text presents. Critical reading can be broken down into three parts: previewing the text, annotating while you read, and summarizing what you've read.

Preview the text before reading it.

Previewing the text involves three main steps:

- **Read the title and any headings and subheadings.** They will provide an outline to help you recall what you already know about the topic.
- **Look for boldface terms.** These may be important concepts or vocabulary words you will need to know.
- **Skim the text.** Start by looking through the introduction, and find the thesis statement. Try to determine the purpose of the text. Are the authors explaining something or trying to convince you to agree with them? Then, skim the paragraphs to get an idea of the writers' main supporting ideas. If you quickly read the beginning and end of each paragraph, you will probably be able to determine the topic of each paragraph and how each one relates to the paragraphs around it. Finally, read the conclusion.

Annotate the text as you read.

When you annotate, you mark up the text and write in the margins. Annotating helps you understand the structure of the text and identify main ideas. It also helps you get beneath the surface of the text and interact with the author's ideas.

Here are some common methods of annotation:

- Underline or highlight main ideas.
- Note unusual insights into the topic.
- If you don't understand something in the text, write a question in the margin.
- If you disagree with something in the text, write a comment in the margin. Note why you disagree.

After reading, summarize the text.

Remember that summarizing a text means stating its main ideas and how they connect with one another. A good summary reflects the author's ideas and opinions—not the reader's. If the writer is making an argument, the summary will trace the logic used in the argument.

You can write the summary in the margin or on a note card. You can even summarize the text mentally. The important thing is to make sure your summary is accurate. If you find you can't summarize the text accurately, reread it.

8-1a | Reading Critically

Directions: *Read the following passage and answer the questions that follow in complete sentences.*

Accelerated or Fast Track Developmental Education is a developmental education reform initiative that is meant to address many of the shortfalls of traditional developmental education programs. As indicated by various studies, attrition amongst development education students, in part, stems from their failure to enroll in the subsequent course in the developmental sequence rather than course failure. In other words, many students placed in a multi-tiered developmental education program either never enroll into their developmental course(s) or drop out between courses in the sequence. The lengthier and more complex the developmental process, the greater the opportunity there is for failure in persistence. In addition, further research suggests that students who place into developmental education courses, but who are permitted to enroll in college level courses, may have a significantly increased chance of completing those college-level course.

1. What is the topic of the passage?

   _____

2. What is the main idea or issue?

   _____

3. Does the passage reach any conclusions? If so, list them.

   _____

4. What audience was this written for? (i.e., general, professional, etc. …)

   _____

5. Which words (list at least five) help you to determine how the author feels about the subject?

   _____

6. What is the purpose of the passage?

   _____

7. What does the term *accelerated* mean in the context of the passage?

   _____

8. What would a good title for the passage?

   _____

| **8-1b** | Reading Critically |

Directions: *Read the following passage. Then, follow the directions and fill in the blanks.*

Digital Integration Initiatives

Most institutions that are non-research based and state funded seem to be late adopters of new instructional and administrative methods. As an HBCU, Malcolm X University has the unique opportunity to be at the vanguard of a burgeoning area of academic and technological development. Since video games, and technology in general, have changed so much in the last decade, it is no wonder that students' attention spans are dwindling. This is a generation that feels obligated to be given everything they want instantly. In other words, this is a generation of instant gratification that has been conditioned to the "Have It Your Way" ideology. So, it is no big surprise that this way of thinking has spilled over into academia. Now, what is the relevance of the aforementioned to Malcolm X University and its students? The answer is simple, Digital Integration Initiatives, which are initiatives that integrate technology into existing traditional academic programs that do not currently make use of digital learning tools.

Digital Integration Initiatives is a concept that combines software with hardware solutions in an effort to create an educational environment that is *tangible* and virtual. Although online courses are currently offered at most area colleges and universities, including Malcom X University, there does not exist a class or course model that allows for traditional and non-traditional students to have the option of working in either environment based upon choice and/or circumstance.

1. Turn the title into a question.

   _____

2. Write the word(s) that help you to determine the topic of the passage.

   _____

3. What is the topic of the passage?

   _____

4. What is the main idea of the passage?

   _____

5. What does the word *tangible* mean as it is used in the passage?

   _____

6. Circle every unfamiliar word and write its definition on separate paper.

8-1c Reading Critically

Directions: *With a partner or group, work with an article or passage provided by your instructor and fill in the blanks below and follow each direction.*

Title: _____

_____

Turn the title into a question: _____

Write the word(s) that is(are) repeated throughout the passage: _____

_____

_____

Topic (drawn from the repeated word(s)): _____

Write **one sentence** for each paragraph that states what the paragraph is about.

Main Idea: _____

_____

Main Idea: _____

_____

Main Idea: _____

_____

Read each of your Main Idea statements and use each to answer the title-derived question that you wrote at the top of this page. Then, you will be able to complete the direction at the bottom of this exercise.

_____

Main Idea of Passage: _____

_____

8-2 | Thinking Critically

Review

Writing a research paper provides you with a forum in which to share your ideas and your unique insights into a topic. You instructor does not want you to simply list what other people think. You need to understand what others have written about the topic, make sense of how their ideas relate, and offer a considered interpretation of those ideas. All this requires you to think about the topic critically.

Thinking critically begins with an analysis of potential sources for your paper. Are they reliable? Are they relevant? How do they support your paper?

Select sources that are reliable.

If you find an article that seems like it might be useful for your paper, determine whether it is reliable. Here are some questions you can ask yourself to help you evaluate a source:

- What are the author's credentials? Is the author an expert on this subject? How do you know? Consider the author's job, education, and research.
- Where was it published? Was it in an academic journal, a respected newspaper or magazine, or on a website run by a reputable organization (such as a university, government agency, or well-established professional organization)? Assess the legitimacy of the periodical or website.
- When was it published? Often, it is important to find the most up-to-date research on a topic, so be especially careful when deciding whether to use articles that were not published recently.

Select sources that are relevant.

If a source is reliable, decide whether it's really relevant. Skim the article to determine whether it will add value to your paper. Will it support or qualify your thesis? Does it offer a point of view you need to consider in your argument? If the answer is yes, use it. If you don't see how it connects to your thesis, discard it.

Determine where your sources will fit in the structure of your paper.

Create a structure for your paper. You can do this in several ways.

- Write a formal outline. An outline lists the main ideas and supporting ideas in a hierarchy, often using Roman numerals and letters to reinforce the hierarchy. Under each idea, list the sources you can use to support it. You may want to note the relevant idea and/or page number in the source so that you can find it easily while writing.
- Create a chart, such as a flow chart, to provide a visual representation of your paper's structure. Use colors, symbols, pictures, and other visual cues to help you organize the information. Think about how each source you select fits into your plan, and note it on the chart.

You may want to create your outline or chart in a large format so that you can use sticky notes to position your research notes. This will allow you to move them around while you work as needed. Remember: You can use notes from one source in different places in your paper. Your paper should not be a list of summaries of your sources but should be organized in a way that best presents your ideas.

8-2a	Thinking Critically

Directions: *In complete sentences, answer the following questions.*

1. If you are given a writing assignment that requires several sources, how would you start the process of finding sources?

   _____

   _____

2. Why did you choose the major that you have selected to study?

   _____

   _____

3. There is a global shortage of fresh water; what are some possible solutions to this problem?

   _____

   _____

4. Do police officers wield too much power?

   _____

   _____

5. Should defaulting on a student loan prevent a person from getting his or her driver's license?

   _____

   _____

8-2b | Thinking Critically

Directions: *Read each of the following statements and identify whether the statement is an assertion based on opinion or an assertion based on verifiable evidence. Explain your responses.*

1. A mile is 5,280 feet.

    Explanation: _____

2. Chocolate is the best flavor of ice cream.

    Explanation: _____

3. Cats are much better pets for single people than dogs are.

    Explanation: _____

4. Houston is located on the Gulf Coast.

    Explanation: _____

5. The scientific name of water is H_2O.

    Explanation: _____

6. The *Mona Lisa* is da Vinci's most famous painting.

    Explanation: _____

7. Electric cars are the best way to combat global warming.

    Explanation: _____

8. The United States is the greatest country on Earth.

    Explanation: _____

9. Medical doctors are one of the highest-earning professions in the world.

    Explanation: _____

10. English should be a required class in all college degree programs around the world, even if the country's native language is not English.

    Explanation: _____

8-2c | Thinking Critically

Directions: *With a partner or a group, fill in the blanks in Column 1: supply statements that you consider to be facts. Then, exchange worksheets with another student; you and your partner should complete Column 2 by providing a brief rationale for each statement, explaining why the statement can be considered a fact.*

Statements	*Rationales*
1. _____	1. _____
_____	_____
2. _____	2. _____
_____	_____
3. _____	3. _____
_____	_____
4. _____	4. _____
_____	_____
5. _____	5. _____
_____	_____
6. _____	6. _____
7. _____	7. _____
_____	_____
8. _____	8. _____
_____	_____
9. _____	9. _____
_____	_____
10. _____	10. _____
_____	_____

8-3		Connecting Ideas to a Larger Picture

Review

If you're writing an argument, your sources can support your research paper in three different ways: to support a main point, to qualify a main point, or to oppose a main point.

Use sources to support your main points.

You will need sources that contain evidence to support your ideas. You can use them to show what experts believe about the topic or what they have discovered in their research about the topic.

For example, if you are writing a paper about the negative impact of stress on students, you will select articles that describe studies that have documented the sorts of negative effects stress has on students and how those effects impacted students' health and lives.

Use sources to qualify your main points.

You will also need sources that define the boundaries of your main points. You might state the conditions under which an idea is valid, such as when, where, or under what circumstances it is true. Make sure to specify exactly which condition you're referring to.

For example, when talking about stress, you would want to specify which kind of stress you're referring to in a specific discussion, such as chronic physical stress, sudden acute emotional stress, or short-term situational stress.

Use sources that can be used in opposition to your main points.

Your readers may not agree with you, so it's important to consider viewpoints that oppose your own. Include the source material that has evidence that supports an opposing view, and then analyze it. Point out any flaws in logic, biased ideas, and facts you consider inconclusive or out-of-date, if relevant, and find evidence to rebut the opposing arguments.

For example, for your paper on stress, you would find articles that argue that stress is helpful. One might argue that stress motivates students to study for exams and even boosts memory. After acknowledging that worry about an exam might induce a student to cram, you would use facts and findings from research to show this is unlikely to be true for most students. You would use your supporting sources to offer evidence that stress can make it hard for students to process what they read or to recall facts or ideas from what they have read, and you might offer statistical evidence on the prevalence and effects of test anxiety.

8-3a Connecting Ideas to a Larger Picture

Directions: *Fill in the blanks with complete sentences that connect the supporting ideas to the main idea.*

Title: Teenagers Are Difficult to Communicate With

Hook: _____

Thesis: *Teens are difficult to communicate with due to attitude, hormones, and social media.*

Topic Sentence 1: _____

    a. Major Detail: _____

       _____

       1. Minor Detail: _____

       _____

Topic Sentence 2: *Although attitude plays a part in teen communication, hormones play an even greater role in teens' ability to communicate effectively.*

    b. Major Detail: _____

       _____

       1. Minor Detail: _____

       _____

Topic Sentence 3: _____

    c. Major Detail: _____

       _____

       1. Minor Detail: _____

       _____

Restatement of Thesis: _____

8-3b | Connecting Ideas to a Larger Picture

Directions: *For each of the following situations, supply responses that describe the connections to self, other texts, and the world implied in the situation. Be sure to answer in complete sentences.*

1. You are a biology major, but you are required to take three history courses to graduate.

    a. Connection to self: _____

    _____

    b. Connection to other texts: _____

    _____

    c. Connection to the world: _____

    _____

2. A state government passes a law to legalize marijuana, but the federal government considers it illegal.

    a. Connection to self: _____

    _____

    b. Connection to other texts: _____

    _____

    c. Connection to the world: _____

    _____

3. All people working in the United States must pay taxes.

    a. Connection to self: _____

    _____

    b. Connection to other texts: _____

    _____

    c. Connection to the world: _____

    _____

4. Talking on a cell phone while driving is not allowed in school zones.

    a. Connection to self: _____

    _____

    b. Connection to other texts: _____

    _____

    c. Connection to the world: _____

    _____

8-3c   Connecting Ideas to a Larger Picture

Directions: *With a partner or as a group, consider the following statements. In complete sentences, explain how each Start relates to its corresponding Outcome. Discuss answers with other groups.*

	Start	*Outcome*
1.	Fewer guns are manufactured.	There is a decrease in emergency room visits.
2.	Students enroll in corequisite courses.	More new homes are sold four years after corequisite policy begins.
3.	Less sugar is used in cereal.	Television advertisement prices drop for morning slots.
4.	Streaming services become faster and proliferate.	Fewer platform video games are sold.
5.	Gambling decreases in Texas.	Banks report record profits in Dallas.
6.	More students are bilingual in 2018.	Mary lost her job as an ESL teacher.
7.	Restrictive immigration laws have passed.	The restaurant industry in California is experiencing widespread employee shortages.
8.	The World Cup is set to be held in Iceland.	Summer wear clothing brands have reported problems obtaining fabric.
9.	A new bio-chip has been developed.	The amount of paper money produced has declined.
10.	New leadership is needed.	No new programs are being approved by the board.

8-4 | Creating Connections Among Facts and Ideas

Review

When doing your research, you'll find a lot of sources. To integrate them into your paper effectively, you need to create connections between the facts, your sources, and your own ideas. Start with an outline or diagram of the planned structure of your paper. Then follow these three steps to integrate your sources:

Map your sources to your main ideas.

You can do this by noting your source on your outline or diagram, whether in the document, on your computer or in a printout. Some students create a poster version of their diagram and use sticky notes to place their sources in it.

Remember that you may want to refer to some of your sources more than once. Be specific in your note so that you can find the right quotation, fact, or idea when you are writing.

Examples of **source notes**:

- Healy, *Great Dissent*, p. 204, Holmes's ref. to JS Mill
- NOAA website: Extended Reconstructed Sea Surface Temperature (ERSST) v3b (graph)

Look for unsupported ideas.

After you've mapped your sources, check to make sure each of your main ideas is supported by at least two sources. If one of your ideas has only one supporting source or none at all, you will need to find more support.

You can fix this problem in one of two ways:

- Look at your current sources again to find facts, details, or opinions that support your point.
- Return to the information-gathering stage and find another source or two that directly pertain to your idea.

Then place the new source notes in your outline or diagram.

Review your sources for apt and up-to-date material.

Now that you've determined how your sources relate to your ideas, look through them again to make sure you've found the best quotations, the most up-to-date statistics, and the most illuminating arguments. Referring to your sources several times as you assemble your paper ensures you're working in a methodical manner.

Remember that you are in charge of your assignment. If, when mapping it, you realize that a particular source isn't helpful, you can leave it out. To make that determination, reread your thesis statement and review your original assignment. Does your source have enough value to remain a part of your project? If not, leave it out.

8-4a	Creating Connections among Facts and Ideas

Directions: *Use the facts and ideas listed below to create sentences that clearly connect.*

1. Fact: There are seven continents.
    Idea 1: Africa is sometimes mistaken as a country by students.
    Idea 2: North America and South America are different continents.

    _____

2. Fact: Cybersecurity is a growing industry.
    Idea 1: Social media has millions of users.
    Idea 2: New cell phone technology makes accessing data relatively simple.

    _____

3. Fact: The United States is a democracy.
    Idea 1: Free speech is being challenged by some politicians.
    Idea 2: The NFL has become a political arena.

    _____

4. Fact: Gun control reform is a controversial subject being discussed in the media.
    Idea 1: Assault weapons are not as common as hunting rifles.
    Idea 2: Restrictions on ammunition sales is a way to impact gun-related crimes.

    _____

5. Fact: A person must be 21 years old to legally consume alcohol.
    Idea 1: A person can vote at age 18 years.
    Idea 2: A person can enlist in the military at age 17.

    _____

6. Fact: The moon orbits the earth.
    Idea 1: Ocean currents are changing.
    Idea 2: Levels of sea water have risen significantly.

    _____

7. Fact: Hurricanes have caused devastating damage in America's southern region.
    Idea 1: Building-supply companies are seeing record profits.
    Idea 2: There is a shortage of skilled construction workers in Texas and Louisiana.

    _____

8-4b   Creating Connections among Facts and Ideas

Directions: *Connect each fact to an idea associated with the field of study identified. Explain your connections using complete sentences.*

1. Fact presented in math class: Pythagorean's theorem is an important concept.
   Field of study: Architecture

   _____

2. Fact presented in English class: Shakespeare introduced many new words into the English language.
   Field of study: Speech Communications

   _____

3. Fact presented in history class: Our modern calendar is based on the Roman calendar.
   Field of study: Computer Science

   _____

4. Fact presented in computer science class: Google is named after the mathematical term *googol*.
   Field of study: Sociology

   _____

5. Fact presented in physics class: Newton's laws of motion provide the framework for all motor-powered movement.
   Field of study: Engineering

   _____

6. Fact presented in political science class: Federal laws are distinct from state laws.
   Field of study: Economics

   _____

7. Fact presented in geography class: Houston is the largest region, in square miles, in Texas.
   Field of study: Environmental Science

   _____

8. Fact presented in biology class: Skin is the largest external organ of the human body.
   Field of study: Chemistry

   _____

8-4c | Creating Connections among Facts and Ideas

Directions: *With a partner or group, use the Internet and find a fact. Create ideas associated with the fact and exchange your ideas with your partner's or group members' to make connections using complete sentences.*

1. Fact: _____
   Idea 1: _____
   Idea 2: _____
   _____
   _____

2. Fact: _____
   Idea 1: _____
   Idea 2: _____
   _____
   _____

3. Fact: _____
   Idea 1: _____
   Idea 2: _____
   _____
   _____

4. Fact: _____
   Idea 1: _____
   Idea 2: _____
   _____
   _____

5. Fact: _____
   Idea 1: _____
   Idea 2: _____
   _____
   _____

8-5 | Annotating and Summarizing Sources

Review

When you are researching a paper, you want to read your sources critically and draw conclusions from them. Two useful skills to help you do this are annotating and summarizing.

Annotate the texts you read.

Before you can summarize a text thoroughly and accurately, you have to understand it. Annotating will help you do that. When you **annotate**, you mark up the text and create notes. This can mean highlighting or underlining important ideas. It may also mean using the margin to jot down questions you have or your responses to ideas in the text.

Examples of **marginal notes**:

- Cf. Tuchman, *First Salute*, p. 118
- Who is Gaspard Monge? Importance?

When you're doing your research using print sources, you may come across other students' annotations. Read them. They may give you further insight into the article.

You can take notes digitally, too. Some students use browser tools to mark up online texts. Database programs have features that allow you to take and refer to notes on the articles you find.

Some students prefer to copy notes longhand onto note cards or into notebooks. Others prefer to read sections or paraphrases of the text aloud and record them for later reference. When you use one of these techniques, make sure you keep a record of the source citation information and the page number for the quotation or other information you recorded.

Summarize each source in your own words.

A **summary** states the most important ideas in a text and shows clearly how they relate to one another.

Never copy someone else's summary of a text. Use your own words. The process of assembling a thorough and accurate summary will help you understand the text.

Also, when you quote material, don't quote from a summary of it. Instead, quote from the full body of the original source.

Review your annotations and summaries.

Remember that you will find a lot of potential sources while doing your research, but you can't use every source you find. Reviewing your annotation and summaries will help you decide which sources will be most relevant and useful when writing your assignment.

| **8-5a** | Annotating and Summarizing Sources |

Directions: *Annotate the text as indicated below. Then, briefly summarize the information in the spaces provided.*

My Teaching Philosophy

The ultimate goal of my teaching is to encourage excellence in achievement. Being an educator at institutions of higher learning for more than two decades, my mission remains the same. I work to help students, who are often underrepresented in higher education, to become independent learners. I wholeheartedly believe that to educate, one must focus on educating the whole person. Thus, my teaching philosophy reflects my desire to aid students in their efforts to take control of their respective academic trajectories through active participation and engagement. To accomplish this goal, I have developed and use a variety of instructional techniques that are aimed at engaging students.

---

1. Turn the title into a question and read the paragraph.

   Title Question: _____

2. Circle the word(s) that are repeated throughout the paragraph to determine the topic.

3. What is the topic of the paragraph?

   Topic: _____

4. Write one sentence that summarizes the paragraph.

   _____

   _____

5. Answer the question you formulated from the title.

   Answer to Title Question: _____

   _____

8-5b | Annotating and Summarizing Sources

Directions: *Develop an annotation and summary of the following passage using the guide below. Circle and define all unfamiliar words.*

Throughout every stage of the criminal justice system, significant racial disparities prevail. Over the last two decades, notable efforts have been made on the federal and state levels to combat evident racial disparities within policing policy. Despite these efforts, the situation persists. The reasons and effects of such stark disparities are subject to a complex and ever-evolving academic discourse and public opinion.

Current research takes into deep consideration many factors that contribute to the racially disproportioned incarcerated groups. Specifically, these factors include crime rates, recidivism, and broader social policy. The following assessment of the query scrutinizes the issue by using leading scholarly research and analysis in the area as its basis. The analysis is not intended to be too narrow in scope but rather more comprehensive in its treatment of the question. By developing a framework of academic inquiries surrounding the problem, a better understanding of the conditions that lead to the issues can be fostered.

Source: Lewis, Wanda (student), "Racial influence on racial disparities in policing." Unpublished. 2009

Summary: Main idea of the work
Relevance: Usefulness of the work
Conclusion: Conclusions presented in the work
Credibility: Reliability of the work

| **8-5c** | Annotating and Summarizing Sources |

Directions: *With a partner or as a group, use the two passages provided by your instructor and follow the steps below in order to complete the two annotations. After you have written your responses in the spaces below, rewrite the Answer to Title Question and each of the Paragraph Summary sentences to create a summary of the source.*

Step 1 – Turn the title into a question and read the passage.

Step 2 – Circle the word(s) that are repeated throughout the passage to determine the topic.

Step 3 – Highlight or underline the first and last sentences of each paragraph.

Step 4 – Write one sentence that summarizes each paragraph.

Step 5 – Answer the question made from the title using the sentences from each paragraph.

Passage 1 Title: _____

Title Question: _____

Topic: _____

Paragraph Summaries: _____

_____

_____

Answer to Title Question:

_____

Passage 2 Title: _____

Title Question: _____

Topic: _____

Paragraph Summaries: _____

_____

_____

Answer to Title Question:

_____

| **9-1** | When and Why to Paraphrase |

Review

When you present your research, you can't just cut-and-paste bits from all your sources into your paper. It would not be clear to the reader how the ideas related to one another. Moreover, the pasted sections would all be written in different styles.

In order to integrate those ideas in a coherent paper, you need to paraphrase them. **Paraphrasing** means using your own words to express someone else's idea.

Know when to paraphrase.

Here are four situations in which you should paraphrase the material from your source:

- when you need to discuss details from the source
- when ideas and facts from the source are more important than its language
- when style, voice, or tone changes from one source to the next
- when the language in the source needs simplifying

In general, it is more appropriate to paraphrase than to quote. Bear in mind that a good paragraph is usually about the same length or longer than the passage you started with.

> Example of **details** in a source: On 11 March 2011, the Pacific experienced and responded to its third destructive local tsunami in three years.

> Source: "List of Tsunamis." *International Tsunami Information Center*, 2018. itic.ioc-unesco.org/index.php?option=com_content&view=category&layout=blog&id=1160&Itemid=1077.

> Example of **paraphrase**: In March 2011, the third devastating local tsunami in as many years struck a Pacific country ("List of Tsunamis").

Remember to use an in-text citation whenever you paraphrase ideas from a source.

Make clear how your ideas and the ideas from your sources relate to one another.

Paraphrasing will help you clarify the interrelationships between the ideas in your paper—whether they are your own or your sources'. Use topic sentences to tell your audience your main idea in that paragraph. Then, readers will know what the paraphrases in a that paragraph have in common.

You can also link the paraphrases with your idea or with each other using transitional expressions that express their relationships.

> Examples of **transitional expressions**: *for example, however, in contrast, moreover, nevertheless, similarly, therefore*

9-1a | When and Why to Paraphrase

Directions: *In the space provided, indicate if paraphrasing is appropriate or not. Write a brief explanation for each response.*

1. If the material is simple and easy to understand.

   _____

2. If the writer is a well-known expert in the area in which the work is being written for.

   _____

3. If all of the information in the work is important.

   _____

4. If you want to avoid long quotes.

   _____

5. If you want to compare and contrast ideas from different scholars.

   _____

6. If you want to demonstrate how your ideas relate to the ideas of other scholars.

   _____

7. If you do not understand the work.

   _____

8. If you want to restate the main idea in your own words for clarity.

   _____

9. If you do not want to cite the original source.

   _____

10. If you do not know the source of a quotation.

    _____

11. If you do not want to refer to the author.

    _____

12. If you want to change the entire meaning of the information.

    _____

9-1b | When and Why to Paraphrase

Directions: *Read the following statements and determine whether it is appropriate to paraphrase. Provide a brief explanation for each response.*

1. Michael finds several sources that seem to provide the same information using slightly different wording.

   _____

2. Elizabeth comes across a source that is written in Spanish, a language that she is fluent in. She decides to use the source for research that is written primarily for an English-speaking audience.

   _____

3. For his job, Eric has been tasked to gather research on the newest computer technology that is scheduled to be released in the next six months. However, Eric is an English major knows very little about computer science. Every source that he finds is written using computer science jargon.

   _____

4. Following her change of major, Bailey decides to consider a few careers. It just so happens that her EDUC 1300 class with Dr. Pamela Bilton-Beard requires a career research paper. Bailey finds several sources that she understands, but they are all saying different things about the same career.

   _____

5. Mia and Yoshiko have a project for their Intro to Speech course. They both gather information and realize that many of their sources are filled with quotes from other sources.

   _____

6. Student Government Association President Afrah Hassan has been tasked with developing an implementation plan for student success. To do so, she is required to do extensive research on the subject. Although she locates very useful information, she must read through pages of irrelevant data.

   _____

9-1c | When and Why to Paraphrase

Directions: *With a partner or group, determine if the paraphrases listed indicate appropriate use of paraphrasing or not. Provide clear explanations for each response.*

I. Original Text:

Dally, Henri. "Leadership in Higher Education." *New Ideas for Innovative Instruction*. Houston Publishing, 2018.

"The international needs of industry fall, in large part, squarely on the shoulders of higher education leaders. The expansion of accessible technology has increased diversity in college classes. Cultural and sub-cultural competencies are major factors in meeting the needs of students that correlate to industry demands. However, higher education leadership must also adapt its approach to addressing shortfalls in institutional operations that do not currently support the connection between higher education and industry."

Paraphrase:

The international needs of industry fall on the shoulders of higher education leaders. This is a major concern. The accessibility of technology is expanding which has increased diversity in college. Cultural and subcultural competencies are major factors in meetings the wants of students and industry. (Dally 3)

_____

_____

II. Original Text:

Charles, Shawndra. "Changes in the Job Market." *Careers for Tomorrow Today*. Minnesota Green Publishing, 2018.

"As technology becomes more prevalent, the job market becomes more technology-driven. Over the past decade, hundreds of low skill jobs have been replaced by technological solutions. Many corporations have invested in robotic and automated processes in lieu of hiring long term operators and warehouse workers. Moreover, outsourcing jobs to foreign companies that provide quality service at a significant discount also attributes to growing changes in the global job market." (Charles 1)

Paraphrase:

The job market is directly impacted by changes in technology. Fewer opportunities for employment without specialized skills are available because companies are opting for technology-based workforce solutions. Also, some jobs are no longer attainable due cost-effective to foreign labor pools.

_____

_____

| **9-2** | Understanding the Ideas of the Source |

Review

Remember that a **paraphrase** says the same thing as the original passage but in different, perhaps clearer, words. After reading your paraphrase, the reader should completely understand the meaning of the original passage.

In order to accurately paraphrase a passage, you have to have a clear and complete understanding of it yourself. It's a good idea to test your understanding of the original passage.

Test your understanding of the original passage.

Start by reading the passage you want to paraphrase. Then imagine that you have a friend who doesn't understand the original passage. How would you explain it? If you have difficulty putting it into your words, reread the passage to see if you've missed anything.

Then, put the passage aside and write your paraphrase from memory in your own words.

Example of an **original passage**: "The new fertilizer act will increase dairy production costs on farms that have expanded rapidly."

Example of a **paraphrase from memory**: Farms that have grown quickly will experience higher production costs as a result of the new law.

Check your paraphrase against the original.

Place your paraphrase side by side with the original passage and compare the two idea by idea. Notice the underlined words in the original sentence: "The new <u>fertilizer</u> act will increase <u>dairy</u> production costs on farms that have expanded rapidly." These are important ideas that are missing in the paraphrase. The paraphrase doesn't identify which law is meant or what kind of farms might experience higher production costs.

After you identify differences in meaning between the original passage and your paraphrase, change your paraphrase as needed, then compare it to the original again. Keep fixing and comparing as needed until you are satisfied that your paraphrase includes all the necessary ideas and that your friend would understand it.

Example of the **final paraphrase**: Dairy farms that have grown quickly will experience higher production costs as a result of the new fertilizer law.

You may need to read the passage several times and write several versions of the paraphrase. Don't worry; that's normal. And remember that you can always take a break. Don't be afraid to move on to another task and return to paraphrasing the passage later.

9-2a	Understanding the Ideas of the Source

Directions: *Read the following original texts. Fill in the blanks as indicated to demonstrate comprehension of the source.*

I.   Original Text:

Dally, Henri. "Leadership in Higher Education." *New Ideas for Innovative Instruction*. Houston Publishing, 2018.

"The international needs of industry fall, in large part, squarely on the shoulders of higher education leaders. The expansion of accessible technology has increased diversity in college classes. Cultural and sub-cultural competencies are major factors in meeting the needs of students that correlate to industry demands. However, higher education leadership must also adapt its approach to addressing shortfalls in institutional operations that do not currently support the connection between higher education and industry."

Topic: _____

Main Idea: _____

Audience: _____

Purpose: _____

Vocabulary: _____

II.   Original Text:

Charles, Shawndra. "Changes in the Job Market." *Careers for Tomorrow Today*. Houston: Minnesota Green Publishing, 2018.

"As technology becomes more prevalent, the job market becomes more technology-driven. Over the past decade, hundreds of low skill jobs have been replaced by technological solutions. Many corporations have invested in robotic and automated processes in lieu of hiring long term operators and warehouse workers. Moreover, outsourcing jobs to foreign companies that provide quality service at a significant discount also attributes to growing changes in the global job market." (Charles 1)

Topic: _____

Main Idea: _____

Audience: _____

Purpose: _____

Vocabulary: _____

| **9-2b** | Understanding the Ideas of the Source |

Directions: *Read the original text provided and explain whether the ideas of the sources are correctly or incorrectly interpreted.*

I.   Original text:

Johnson and Tran present the idea that life on other planets can possibly exist if very specific conditions are met (12).

Paraphrase:

Johnson and Tran say that alien life definitely exists.

II.   Original text:

According Henrich Goldenberg, in case of a sudden hurricane, it is wise to keep emergency supplies (201).

Paraphrase:

To not be killed during a hurricane, Goldenberg says you must have food, water, and other supplies.

III.   Original text:

Fleming asserts that eco-tourism is a viable means to ecology and economically sustain areas in danger of population (33).

Paraphrase:

Eco-tourism is an eco-friendly and cost-effective way to minimize negative impact on the environment (Fleming, 33).

IV.   Original text:

According to Kevin Clement, "the probability of an extinction level event occurring in the next ten years is very high due to escalating global conflicts and unpredictable weather phenomena" (100).

Paraphrase:

An extinction level event is going to happen in ten years.

9-2c | Understanding the Ideas of the Source

Directions: *With a partner or as a group, complete the following statements with original ideas. Then, exchange with a partner or within a group and have someone paraphrase the completed statements. Review the statement and indicate whether the original ideas have been correctly or incorrectly interpreted in the paraphrase.*

I. At the beginning of each school year, students often _____.

Paraphrase:

_____.

Correct interpretation _____   Incorrect Interpretation _____

II. _____ (insert last name) asserts that new methods of travel have made the world more accessible due to _____ .

Paraphrase:

_____.

Correct interpretation _____   Incorrect Interpretation _____

III. _____ (insert two last names) state that more _____ has resulted in fewer _____ for millennials.

Paraphrase:

_____.

Correct interpretation _____   Incorrect Interpretation _____

IV. Children born with _____ have a higher chance of developing _____ since both parents are _____.

Paraphrase:

_____.

Correct interpretation _____   Incorrect Interpretation _____

V. Cartoons have become _____ because there are _____ since the start of _____.

Paraphrase:

_____.

Correct interpretation _____   Incorrect Interpretation _____

9-3 | When Paraphrasing Doesn't Work

Review

When writing a paper, you should usually paraphrase ideas and information you have found in your research. But there are times when paraphrasing isn't appropriate.

Summarize to give the general idea.

Sometimes you don't need to communicate the details of a specific passage. Instead, you need to give a general idea of what the author said in a paragraph, an article, or even a book. That's when you need to **summarize**.

> Example of a **summary of a novel**: In Sir Walter Scott's **Ivanhoe**, the young knight Ivanhoe returns from the Crusades to find England suffering under the corrupt rule of King John. With the help of the mysterious Black Knight, Ivanhoe and his companions succeed in restoring the throne to the rightful king.

If you need the author's exact words, quote.

There are several cases when it is best to quote a passage rather than paraphrase:

- Sometimes it is the writer's exact words that are important, and paraphrasing them would lose the point. This is often true in literature, when the specific words of a poet, playwright, or novelist phrase the ideas so well that they would lose something by being paraphrased. It may also be true of iconic texts, such as the Declaration of Independence or the Gettysburg Address.

  > Example of **quotation from a poem**: "… evening is spread out against the sky/Like a patient etherized upon a table" (Eliot)

  > Example of a **quotation from an iconic text**: "We hold these truths to be self-evident, that all men are created equal, that they are endowed by their Creator with certain unalienable Rights, that among these are Life, Liberty and the pursuit of Happiness" (*Declaration of Independence*).

- To share technical language or statistics, quote rather than paraphrasing. If you were to paraphrase, you might well be inaccurate.

  > Example of a **technical quotation**: A digital signal processor "is a highly customized processor designed to perform signal manipulation calculations at high speed" (Kinder).

- If a passage is so clear and concise that you couldn't improve it by paraphrasing it, quote it.

  > Example of a **concise quotation**: "Music has charms to soothe the savage breast" (Congreve).

To decide whether to quote or to paraphrase, ask yourself if your readers need the exact words or if your own wording would communicate better.

| **9-3a** | When Paraphrasing Doesn't Work |

Directions: *Discuss why the paraphrasing is inappropriate for the situations described.*

1. If the writer only changes one word in the paraphrased statement.

_____

2. If the writer includes all information from the source, despite its relevance.

_____

3. If the writer excludes the citation of the source.

_____

4. If the writer uses more challenging language than the source.

_____

5. If the writer reuses words or phrases directly from the source.

_____

6. If the writer does not understand the source and makes up the information.

_____

7. If the writer copies a paraphrase from another source of the original source.

_____

8. If the writer changes the facts of the source.

_____

9. If the writer includes more information than the original source provided.

_____

10. If the writer moves words around in the sentences from the source.

_____

11. If the writer does not acknowledge the author of the original source.

_____

12. If the writer attributes technical information to common knowledge.

_____

9-3b | When Paraphrasing Doesn't Work

Directions: *Read the following statements and explain why the paraphrase did not work for each statement.*

1. Original Statement: Unpredictable weather patterns make it difficult to plan for vacations during the fall (Helge 12).

   Paraphrase: No one can take vacations during the fall because of unpredictable weather (Helge).

   _____

2. Original Statement: Neshon Jackson asserts that free college is the best way to increase college completion rates (Jackson 15).

   Paraphrase: Jackson asserts that free college is the way to increase college completion rates.

   _____

3. Original Statement: Student loan default is a major driver for developmental education reform (Gallo 4).

   Paraphrase: Students do not default on loans (Gallo 4).

   _____

4. Original Statement: Over population of some species leads to environmental issues in the years that follow (Hunter 392).

   Paraphrase: Over population leads to problems in the environment (hunter).

   _____

5. Original Statement: Recent decreases in persistence has prompted colleges to re-evaluate their strategic plans (Deight 34).

   Paraphrase: New strategic plans are being drafted due to decreases in persistence (Davids 5).

   _____

6. Original Statement: It is not necessary to be an authority on video games to appreciate their appeal (Vincent 41).
   Paraphrase: Just because you don't have computer science degree doesn't mean you do not appreciate video games.

   _____

7. Original Statement: Tomi Middleton believes that hard work yields great rewards (Middleton 9).
   Paraphrase: Hard work yields great rewards.

   _____

9-3c | When Paraphrasing Doesn't Work

Directions: *With a partner or as a group, read the following statements and determine why paraphrasing does not work given the contexts. Provide explanations for each response.*

1. If you do not understand the source.

    _____

    _____

2. If you have only rearranged words from the source in the paraphrase.

    _____

    _____

3. If you copy the source verbatim for the paraphrase.

    _____

    _____

4. If you add more information to the original source in the paraphrase.

    _____

    _____

5. If you include irrelevant information from the source in the paraphrase.

    _____

    _____

6. If you do not give credit to the author of the source in the paraphrase.

    _____

    _____

7. If you change facts from the source in the paraphrase.

    _____

    _____

8. If you improperly cite the source in the paraphrase.

    _____

    _____

9-4 | Changing Words and Sentence Structure

Review

Paraphrasing is putting the author's ideas into your own words. But you can't just replace a few of the words and leave the rest as is. That's called *patchwriting*, and it's a type of plagiarism.

Change the words and the sentence structure.

To paraphrase properly, you have to change not only the words, but also the sentence structure. That will require changing the word order, using different parts of speech, and perhaps changing the voice (from passive to active, for example).

Look at this sentence: "Today, critics and audiences both may find *The Taming of the Shrew* sexist and *All's Well That Ends Well* contrived." Now look at these paraphrases.

> Example of a **faulty paraphrase**: Nowadays, people may find *The Taming of the Shrew* chauvinistic and *All's Well That Ends Well* artificial.

This paraphrase doesn't work because the words *nowadays*, *people*, *chauvinistic*, and *artificial* have simply been slotted into the original sentence in place of other words. Also, *people* is a lot more general than "critics and audiences."

> Example of an **effective paraphrase**: *The Taming of the Shrew* and *All's Well That Ends Well* are no longer as well-received as they once were; the former is often considered chauvinistic, and the latter artificial.

Notice that the voice has been changed from active to passive. Because the topic is plays, it can be inferred that their reception would be among drama critics and theatergoers. The adverb *today* at the beginning of the original sentence has become the adverb *no longer* in the middle of the paraphrase. The second sentence uses a semicolon to separate a clause identifying the plays from a clause, explaining how they are received nowadays. The two sentences now have completely different sentence structures and wording while imparting the same information.

Check that your paraphrase is complete and accurate.

It takes practice to learn to paraphrase effectively. Even professional writers need a few tries to create a satisfactory paraphrase. To check that your paraphrase is complete and accurate, ask yourself these questions:

- Did I leave out any relevant information?
- Did I change the meaning when I changed the words?

To get the best results, have someone read your paraphrase first, then the source. Did your reader learn anything new from reading the original source? If so, your paraphrase still needs work.

To check your own paraphrase, read it, and then read the original. Do both versions mean the same thing? If so, you have paraphrased successfully. If not, try again. Remember that writing is a process. Don't be discouraged if it takes several tries to write a paraphrase that works.

9-4a	Changing Words and Sentence Structure

Directions: *Write a paraphrase for each part of the sentence two different ways.*

Original Sentence:

The legal age that a person can join the military in the US is 18 years of age, but, in most cases, a person must be 21 years old before he or she is able to legally buy or consume alcohol.

I.   *The legal age that a person can join the military in the US is 18 years of age,*

    1.   _____

    2.   _____

II.   *but*

    3.   _____

    4.   _____

III.   a person must be 21 years old before he or she is able to legally buy or consume alcohol.

    5.   _____

    6.   _____

IV.   Combine the 3 different sentence rewrites to create paraphrases.

    7.   _____

        _____

        _____

        _____

    8.   _____

        _____

        _____

        _____

| **9-4b** | Changing Words and Sentence Structure |

Directions: *Write a paraphrase for each part of the sentence two different ways.*

Original Sentence:

The current rate of unemployment indicates growth in the job market; however, some economists have predicted a gradual slowing of hiring trends due to recent legislation.

I. *The current rate of unemployment indicates growth in the job market;*

1. _____

2. _____

II. *however,*

3. _____

4. _____

III. *some economists have predicted a gradual slowing of hiring trends due to recent legislation.*

5. _____
_____

6. _____
_____

IV. Combine the 2 different sentence rewrites from Parts I, II and III to create paraphrases.

7. _____
_____
_____
_____

8. _____
_____
_____
_____

9-4c	Changing Words and Sentence Structure

Directions: *With a partner or a group, create a sentence that can be divided into two parts and number the parts of the original sentence. Then, fill in the blanks in below, and exchange with others. Write a paraphrase for each part of the sentence two different ways.*

Original Sentence:

_____

_____

I. *Part I of Sentence:* _____

    1. _____

    2. _____

II. *Part II of Sentence:* _____

    3. _____

    4. _____

III. *Part III of Sentence:* _____

    5. _____

    6. _____

IV. Combine the 2 different sentence rewrites to create paraphrases.

    7. _____

        _____

        _____

        _____

    8. _____

        _____

        _____

        _____

9-5 | Identifying Your Source

Review

When writing a research paper, you must credit the sources of all the information you use. This includes paraphrases, summaries, and quotations. Citing your sources tells your readers what you say is credible.

Document your sources using a recognized citation method.

Your professors will probably tell you which citation method they want you to use in your research paper. Three common methods are MLA, APA, and CMS. MLA style is commonly used in literature and the humanities. APA style is used in psychology and the social sciences. CMS is commonly used in publishing.

Each citation method has its own documentation format.

- MLA uses a brief citation in the text and a Works Cited list on a separate page at the end.

  Example of an **MLA in-text citation**: The jester's wordplay adds some comic relief to an otherwise tense scene: "fool as I am, I shall not do your fool's errand" (Scott 187).
  Example of an **MLA Word Cited entry**: Scott, Walter. *Ivanhoe*. Barnes & Noble Classics, 2005.

- APA also uses in-text citations and a page of References at the end.

  Example of an **APA in-text citation**: "There are many ways in which a lack of sufficient sleep will kill you" (Walker, 2017, p. 134).
  Example of an **APA reference list entry**: Walker, M. (2017). *Why we sleep: Unlocking the power of sleep and dreams*. Scribner.

- CMS uses footnotes (at the foot of the page) or endnotes (at the end of the text). The reader is directed to the note by a small raised number after the information in the running text.

  Example of a ***CMS* footnote/endnote**: Warner points out the difficulty of using a placebo as a control[1] while studying the effects of diet on human health.
  1. Anthony Warner, *The Angry Chef: Bad Science and the Truth about Healthy Eating* (London: Oneworld Publications, 2017), 176.

Use signal phrases to differentiate paraphrases from your own ideas.

You must clearly indicate transitions between your ideas and those of your sources. A good way to do this is with a **signal phrase**. A signal phrase often refers to the author or title of the source you used. Since the name is in the phrase, the in-text citation does not need to include it.

  Example of a **signal phrase**: We all need sleep. As Walker points out, not getting enough sleep can easily be fatal (2017, p. 134).

9-5a	Identifying Your Source

Directions: *Read each paraphrase and identify its source in the space provided.*

1. Paraphrase: The new method of dating has moved to the digital realm via social media for the 21ˢᵗ century.

   Source: _____

2. Paraphrase: According to Lin, the best approach to deal with poor communication is by writing (2000).

   Source: _____

3. Paraphrase: Students should work fewer hours (Evans 45).

   Source: _____

4. Paraphrase: Nursing is a high paying career (Nnuko 118-122).

   Source: _____

5. Paraphrase: His sense of self is always questioned based on his behavior (Lovelady & Jones, 2013, p.12).

   Source: _____

6. Paraphrase: In Reed's Joyful Sunday, the hero kills the villain with a spoon (De Los Santos 19).

   Source: _____

7. Paraphrase: There are still many *new species* to be discovered in the oceans (Knight & Goin, 2001).

   Source: _____

8. Paraphrase: Harper is a great singer.

   Source: _____

9. Paraphrase: As noted in the Edward's *Opinions*, the concept of love is too expansive to define.

   Source: _____

10. Paraphrase: Jenkins says that "technology is growing too fast" (Khalid 76).

    Source: _____

11. Paraphrase: Prichett and Novak believe that more faculty is needed immediately.

    Source: _____

12. Paraphrase: Without trust, a marriage falls apart and may never be whole again (Ganders 90).

    Source: _____

| **9-5b** | Identifying Your Source |

Directions: *Read each of the following cited passages. Create paraphrases for the underlined sentences that clearly identify the source.*

I. Original Text:

My pedagogic approach is shaped by the core idea that my instructional methods should allow students to naturally retain and process the information provided in order to be able to apply it to critical thinking skills. <u>Learning is a process that takes time and focus; moreover, learning to learn is an even more daunting process to fully comprehend for many students. Nevertheless, I believe that students should not only be given the proper tools for success, but also shown how to apply those theoretical tools to immediate real-life applications.</u> Therefore, I incorporate contextualization to all aspects of my teaching. I also leave myself open to learning from others, including students. By establishing such a reciprocal relationship within learning environments creates an atmosphere that is conducive for shared deep learning experiences. Francis, Kiwana. <u>My Teaching Philosophy</u>. 3rd ed. (2004). 12-15.

Paraphrase: _____

_____

_____

_____

Source: _____

II. Original Text:

<u>Duster's article is relevant for developing a historical understanding of the conditions by which development education initiatives can be attributed to. Disparate conditions of disenfranchised groups yield environments that can stunt progression in many aspects for several decades that follow the cession of the practices that cause said conditions.</u> Therefore, gaps in understanding experienced by developmental students today are, in part, a by-product of defunct social practices. Equitable access measures in higher education are necessary to avoid the practice of "systemic replication of privilege in society" (Pho, 2003, p. 223).

Paraphrase: _____

_____

_____

_____

Source: _____

9-5c	Identifying Your Source

Directions: *With a partner or as a group, write a paraphrase based on passages provided by your instructor and exchange. Identify the source for each paraphrase in the space provided.*

1. Paraphrase: _____

   Source: _____

2. Paraphrase: _____

   Source: _____

3. Paraphrase: _____

   Source: _____

4. Paraphrase: _____

   Source: _____

5. Paraphrase: _____

   Source: _____

6. Paraphrase: _____

   Source: _____

7. Paraphrase: _____

   Source: _____

8. Paraphrase: _____

   Source: _____

9. Paraphrase: _____

   Source: _____

10. Paraphrase: _____

    Source: _____

11. Paraphrase: _____

    Source: _____

12. Paraphrase: _____

    Source: _____

10-1 | When and Why to Write Summaries

Review

In your writing, share the main point of a source using a summary.

A **summary** is a brief restatement of a source's main ideas. Summarizing a source allows you to reduce the ideas of a passage or a whole work to a manageable chunk of information. You can share the main point of a paragraph using a single sentence. In a paragraph-long summary, you can present a shortened version of the main point of a longer work.

> Example of a source: Most people experience some kind of pain during their lives. Pain serves an important purpose: it warns the body when it's in danger. Think of when your hand touches a hot stove. But ongoing pain causes distress and affects quality of life. Pain is the number one reason people see a doctor. ("Managing Pain: Moving Beyond Opioids")

> Example of a summary: Pain indicates something is wrong, but chronic pain disrupts lives and is the most common complaint among patients.

Use summaries to achieve particular purposes.

Writing a summary is useful for two main reasons: First, a summary helps you condense big ideas from your source into just a few lines in your paper. You can use a summary for different purposes. For example, you can quickly demonstrate the major differences between two viewpoints. You can also use a summary to provide background before moving into your own discussion. Use a quotation or paraphrase instead of a summary if you need to give your reader specific details, such as a fact, statistic, or precise statement.

When you are working with multiple viewpoints or arguments, summarizing them allows you to present the ideas of two or more sources in a single paragraph. When you integrate summaries, however, be sure to use signal phrases and to include documentation of the source to give clear credit for ideas and information that are not your own.

Second, writing a summary helps to check your comprehension of the source. Accurately summarizing a source shows you understand it.

Know when and how to summarize.

A summary must be *all* your own words.

A summary should be brief, identifying the author's thesis and conveying the main points of the original in concise, clear language.

Name the source's author and the title of the work at the outset of your summary. Include page numbers where the passage appears, if appropriate.

Take care to summarize accurately. Use objective language and be careful not to unintentionally distort the author's meaning.

If you find it necessary to include some particularly apt words from the original source, be sure to set them off in quotation marks. Record the page number where the quotation appears.

10-1a | When and Why to Write Summaries

Directions: *For each situation listed, indicate whether summarizing is appropriate, and briefly explain why.*

1. You have not read the material.

   _____

2. You have read material that is lengthy.

   _____

3. You are asked to write an annotated bibliography.

   _____

4. You are analyzing one sentence.

   _____

5. You are using scholarly articles to research a topic.

   _____

6. You want to develop an understanding of an article's (or book's, or passage's) main idea.

   _____

7. You are unclear about vocabulary being used.

   _____

8. You find a source that is only available in a language that you do not speak or read.

   _____

9. You are summarizing a summary.

   _____

10. You do not understand the material.

    _____

11. You want to put the material in your own words for better comprehension.

    _____

12. You want to paraphrase a summary.

    _____

13. You do not follow the writer's pattern of development.

    _____

10-1b | When and Why to Write Summaries

Directions: *Answer the following questions in complete sentences; please explain your answers.*

1. When is it appropriate to write a summary?

   _____

2. What is the purpose of a summary?

   _____

3. How do you develop the title of a summary?

   _____

4. How do you develop the main idea of a summary?

   _____

5. Does a summary include every detail?

   _____

6. Should a summary include your thoughts?

   _____

7. Should you use sentences directly from the source in the summary?

   _____

8. Do summaries include additional information beyond what the source provides?

   _____

9. Can you change the facts in a summary?

   _____

10. Can a summary be written in a different order of development from the source's development?

    _____

11. Should a summary be written after you have read the material? If so, why?

    _____

12. Does a summary include the main idea of the source?

    _____

13. Should a summary include paraphrasing?

    _____

10-1c | When and Why to Write Summaries

Directions: *With a partner or as a group, think of five situations in which writing a summary is appropriate and five situations in which it is not appropriate. Exchange worksheets and determine whether you agree that your fellow students' situations are correctly categorized. Briefly explain your responses in complete sentence and discuss with your partner or group.*

Example: *Situation:* An assignment asks students to read different novels and discuss each chapter in group presentations.

> *Explanation:* This is an appropriate situation to write a summary because a novel is too long to discuss page by page.

1. Situation: _____

   Explanation: _____

2. Situation: _____

   Explanation: _____

3. Situation: _____

   Explanation: _____

4. Situation: _____

   Explanation: _____

5. Situation: _____

   Explanation: _____

6. Situation: _____

   Explanation: _____

7. Situation: _____

   Explanation: _____

8. Situation: _____

   Explanation: _____

9. Situation: _____

   Explanation: _____

10. Situation: _____

    Explanation: _____

| **10-2** | Reading and Writing to Create a Summary |

Review

To write a good summary, you need to understand the source you're summarizing. To fully understand it, you may need to read the text several times.

Identify the main ideas and supporting details.

Start by highlighting the main idea or ideas. You may find them in the introduction, conclusion, or both. This will be the author's own summary of their conclusions.

Then, locate the details that support or defend the author's main ideas. In shorter texts, these might be the topic sentences of paragraphs. In longer articles, you may have to read groups of paragraphs to find this information. In books, you may have to read still longer sections, such as chapters, to find the supporting details that support the thesis. Highlight or mark the supporting details in a different way.

Finally, make a list or outline of the main ideas and major supporting details. Use accurate paraphrases. After writing the list, check to make sure it includes all the important points; add any that are missing. Ask yourself whether all of the details on your list are needed to clearly explain the author's thinking; cross out any that aren't needed. Revise your list as necessary.

Draft your summary in your own words.

Referring to your list—but without looking at the source—write your summary. Remember that a summary includes only the main ideas and major supporting details. Don't include any minor points.

Check your summary for accuracy and clarity.

The next step is to read and revise your summary as needed.

First, compare your summary with the source. Make sure you included the main ideas and major details. Make sure you used only your own words, but remember to keep them academic, or somewhat formal, in tone.

Remember that a good summary clarifies the author's thinking, so make sure you have used transitions to emphasize the logical connections between ideas. Add them as needed.

> Examples of **transitions**: *as a result, at the same time, because, consequently, however, in conclusion, in contrast, moreover, nevertheless*

Then, reread your summary without looking at the source. Does it make sense? If possible, have a friend read it and tell you what they learned from it. Check their understanding against what the source says. If they grasp the author's main ideas and logic, you have written a successful summary.

Document your source.

Use the assigned citation style to document your source. You will need to use signal phrases in the text to introduce the source material, as well as in-text citations and a reference list.

> Examples of **signal phrases**: *Walker explains… ; according to Piaget… ; Poe tells the story of…*

10-2a | Reading and Writing to Create a Summary

Directions: *Read the following paragraphs. As you read, summarize each paragraph. Then combine your summaries to create one overall summary below. Then construct your summary in the space below.*

An Examination of Alex Haley's *Roots*

Notes for Your Summary

Alex Haley's *Roots* expresses the concept of fear via various mediums, including indentured servitude, punishment and religion. Each of these tools of control is wielded without impunity throughout the novel. Thus, Haley presents a graphic and dynamic image of the horrific business that has become known as the peculiar institution. Moreover, the notion of fear acts the underlying theme for the entire plot, as it does for actual life.

Slavery is the main means that Haley employs to display one form of fear. In the work, Africans, and those who would become African-Americans, are subjected to indignities that are unimaginable. Probably the most memorable of these atrocities comes from a scene in the story where Kunte Kinte is forced to accept his new "Christian" identity. He is asked several times to answer to the name "Toby". When he refuses to acknowledge this request, half of one of his feet is chopped off. Thus, he is destined to remain a slave because he no longer possesses the ability to run. His mobility is permanently inhibited. In addition, the severing of Kinte's foot can also be applied to yet another form of fear, punishment.

Fear rears its ugly head in the novel through different types of punishment. As previously mentioned, Kunte Kinte receives a swift and severe penalty for his insubordinate actions. During the time frame of *Roots,* blacks are considered chattel. Hence, they are judged under an alternative set of rules from white individuals. To maintain control over the population of slaves in the work, lynchings, beatings, rapes, non-surgical amputations and murders are often committed. These inhumane treatments achieve their desired effect, fear. Even when slaves have abandoned all hope of a worldly salvation from their torturous existence, whites enter religious realms to extend their reign of terror.

Summary

_____

_____

_____

_____

_____

10-2b | Reading and Writing to Create a Summary

Directions: *Review the following assignment. Then, using your own words, fill in the blanks at the bottom to write a summary of the assignment.*

Varying Sentence Structure

Directions: *Revise the paragraphs below. Use a variety of sentence types (simple, compound, complex and compound-complex) in the revisions.*

I. Technological advancements made it possible for people to illegally release movies and music over the internet. There was little to no regulations for this type of piracy. Billions of dollars in revenue was lost annually. Many people lost jobs. These jobs have not come back. Legislation had to be passed to address the issue. The problem still exists. There are laws that been instituted to combat this type of piracy.

II. International students face many challenges. They come to the United States. Some of the challenges are expected. Others are not as evident. The world has become a much smaller place over the last decade. Cultures that were once totally isolated from the Western Hemisphere are now able to peer into American culture from afar. This is voyeuristic examination of America's social structure. It gives foreigners a once rare opportunity to see the United States clearly. Issues arise for the fortunate few who travel to America in search of intellectual and personal pursuits. It can be said that international students face a large amount of academic ans social challenges.

Title: _____

Main Idea: _____

Topic 1: _____

Topic 2: _____

Summary

_____

_____

_____

_____

_____

10-2c | Reading and Writing to Create a Summary

Directions: *With a partner or as a group, copy an original paragraph from an essay or journal article. Give it a title. Exchange worksheets and fill in the blanks as indicated. Discuss responses.*

(Insert paragraph)

_____

_____
_____
_____
_____
_____
_____
_____
_____
_____
_____
_____
_____

Title: _____

Main Idea: _____

Topic 1: _____

Topic 2: _____

Topic 3: _____

Summary

_____
_____
_____
_____
_____

10-3 | Avoiding Interpretation

Review

Be objective when you summarize ideas from a source.

A good summary is fair and objective. Make sure you are stating the author's ideas, not your own. In a summary, never include your opinion of the author's ideas or evaluate their argument.

After writing a summary, reread it. Does it present the author's ideas clearly, completely, and fairly? If you see that you've added your own opinion to the summary, remove it.

State your opinion only after completing the summary.

Make it obvious to your readers that the summary has ended before you give your opinion.

To do this, complete the summary, and place an in-text citation at the end. Then, introduce your opinion using a clear transition. Adding the author's name to the sentence following the transition will give readers an additional clue that what follows is your opinion.

> Example of a **source text**: The general use of speech is to transfer our mental discourse into verbal, or the train of our thoughts into a train of words, and that for two commodities; whereof one is the registering of the consequences of our thoughts, which being apt to slip out of our memory and put us to a new labor, may again be recalled by such words as they were marked by. So that the first use of names is to serve for marks or notes of remembrance. Another is when many use the same words to signify, by their connection and order one to another, what they conceive or think of each matter; and also what they desire, fear, or have any other passion for. And for this use they are called signs. Special uses of speech are these: first, to register what by cogitation we find to be the cause of anything, present or past; and what we find things present or past may produce, or effect; which, in sum, is acquiring of arts. Secondly, to show to others that knowledge which we have attained; which is to counsel and teach one another. Thirdly, to make known to others our wills and purposes that we may have the mutual help of one another. Fourthly, to please and delight ourselves, and others, by playing with our words, for pleasure or ornament, innocently.

> Example of a **faulty summary**: In *Leviathan*, Hobbes says that speech enables us to turn thoughts into words, so the thoughts can be remembered and communicated to others—a very limited view. He offers an incomplete list of what speech allows humans to do: to pass on what we have learned to others, to ask for help, and to engage in wordplay (Chapter 4, par. 3).

> Example of a **good summary**: In *Leviathan*, Hobbes says that speech enables us to turn thoughts into words, so the thoughts can be remembered and communicated to others. Thus, speech allows us to learn, to pass on what we have learned to others, to ask for help, and to engage in wordplay (Chapter 4).

> Example of an **opinion statement**: However, Hobbes understates the value of speech.

10-3a | Avoiding Interpretation

Directions: *Read the following passage. Answer the questions in complete sentences based on the passage.*

Urban and Rural Community Colleges

Urban and rural community colleges are vital components in affording Americans greater access to higher education. With over one thousand community colleges spread out across the nation, these colleges' varied goals and missions are reflective of their surrounding communities' needs. That said, what are the key differences between urban and rural community colleges? Moreover, what are some of the different challenges facing large and small community colleges? To address these questions, one can look at factors such as size, populations served, and community needs, which can be reflected in the differing challenges (accessibility, remediation, and funding) facing large and small community colleges.

1. What is the title?

   _____

2. What is the topic?

   _____

3. What is the main idea?

   _____

4. How does the title relate to the main idea?

   _____

5. Based on the main idea, what will be topic of the next paragraph?

   _____

6. Are there any supporting details for the main idea?

   _____

Write a summary of the passage in fewer sentences than the passage.

_____

_____

_____

10-3b | Avoiding Interpretation

Directions: *Answer the following questions in complete sentences.*

1. Does a summary include your opinion? Why or why not?

    _____

2. When summarizing, should you include your new ideas about the topic?

    _____

3. If you don't know the meaning of a term used in a source, should you write the summary based on what you think the term(s) means?

    _____

4. Should a summary be longer than the source because it involves analysis of the information?

    _____

5. In a summary, should the writer always include information from other sources for clarity?

    _____

6. Should a summary include key points from the source?

    _____

7. Does the summary need to develop in the same sequence as the source?

    _____

8. In a summary, should you state whether you agree or disagree with the source?

    _____

9. Does a summary focus mainly on the facts presented in the source?

    _____

10. Do you need to understand the source before summarizing it?

    _____

11. Are summaries and analyses the same thing?

    _____

12. Should your summary have a different title than the title the source uses?

    _____

10-3c | Avoiding Interpretation

Directions: *With a partner or a group, write a paragraph in the space below. Exchange paragraphs and write a summary based on the paragraph you receive. Discuss responses.*

Paragraph:

_____

_____

_____

_____

_____

_____

_____

_____

_____

_____

Summary:

_____

_____

_____

_____

_____

_____

| **10-4** | Using Summaries in an Annotated Bibliography |

Review

Use summaries when compiling an annotated bibliography.

In addition to using summaries in the body of a research paper, you can use them to compile an annotated bibliography of your research. An annotated bibliography is a list of sources with information about each. Your instructor may require you to create an annotated bibliography as part of your research assignment.

However, even if it's not required, preparing an annotated bibliography is helpful because it will remind you what information is in each source, why you thought the source useful, and where to find the source in case you need to refer to it again. Having an annotated bibliography can save you from having to reread your sources.

Begin your annotated bibliography entry with a description of your source.

To describe your source, you need two things: a complete bibliographic citation and a summary.

To create the bibliographic citation, follow the formatting rules of the citation style your instructor has asked you to use. Remember that the citations for different types of texts are formatted differently. Follow the rules for the type of text you have read: a book, an article in a periodical, an online article, a video, or some other type of media or publication.

Below the citation, write an objective summary of the ideas in the source. Remember *not* to include your opinion of the topic or the source.

Complete your annotated bibliography entry with an evaluation of your source.

Below the summary, write a paragraph explaining the value of the source for your research. The author might provide a convincing argument in support of a particular point you want to make. Conversely, they might make a counterargument you can refute in your paper. The article might provide background for the topic your paper investigates. The bibliography in the source might contain references to other articles you want to read. You can also include useful information such as notes on the author's credibility or references to related articles.

Example of an **annotated bibliography entry**:

Crowley, J. L. (2006). What does it mean to see? A historical review of the emergence of computer vision. In D. Söffker, E. Ahle, & W. Luther (Eds.), *Guidance and control of autonomous systems* (pp. 85–127). Logos.

Crowley traces visual perception in machines from the "seeing robots" of the 1960s through computer image analysis and interpretation in the 1990s to realtime vision systems in the early twenty-first century. He explores the mathematical foundations for each of these developments.

This article reproduces a lecture given at a 2005 conference. Crowley clearly explains the theories and mathematics underlying each development. There are many visuals, including diagrams, photos, and graphs. It's out-of-date but provides good historical background.

| **10-4a** | Using Summaries in an Annotated Bibliography |

Directions: *Answer the following questions in complete sentences.*

1. What is an annotated bibliography?

_____

2. What is included in an annotated bibliography?

_____

3. What does the summary in an annotated bibliography tell the reader?

_____

4. Should the summary be as long as the source? If so, explain why?

_____

5. Should the summary include all major and minor details from the source? If so, explain why?

_____

6. In an annotated bibliography, does the summary need to be unrelated to the topic of the work that the annotated bibliography will be used for?

_____

7. Does the summary's language need to be more technical than the source's language?

_____

8. Can the summaries be used to compare sources listed in an annotated bibliography?

_____

9. Does the annotation include an evaluation of the source?

_____

10. Is the author's credibility discussed in the summary?

_____

11. Should the summary describe the methods an author used during his or her writing process?

_____

12. Does the summary of the annotated bibliography provide a synopsis of the source?

_____

10-4b   Using Summaries in an Annotated Bibliography

Directions: *Read the following annotated bibliography entry. Underline the summary part of the annotation. Then, answer the questions that follow.*

Ramirez, J. (2012). *No mas: Practices in developmental education.* Mexia Foundational Center for
Developmental Education, Noam State University.

(1) The book is the result of a collaborative effort between the Continuous Quality Improvement Network (CQIN) and the National Center for Developmental Education (NCDE). (2) It acts as the gold standard for research-based best practices for developmental education. (3) However, I do not like it. Its approach to cohesively presenting value of developmental education best practices uses organizational, administrative, and institutional practices; instruction practices; and customization of the best practices as the foundation for framing a coherent model to more effectively serve underprepared students. (4) Nevertheless, the approach would have been better if it included more data about college-ready students. (5) Also, the work presented the most relevant available data on successful methods used by practitioners in isolation, yet it claims to be a repository of developmental education tools that can be implemented and configured in multiple ways within existing higher education infrastructures. (6) Each best practice is followed by tips for implementation.

(7) The information provided by the work is invaluable. (8) It identifies and presents virtually all information known regarding developmental education. (9) Therefore, it is a guidebook for understanding the ins and outs of modern developmental education. (10) As its title suggests, the book identifies what should be done and proposes ways to accomplish the necessary efforts to yield student success.

1. Who is the author of the source? _____

2. What is the main idea of the summary? _____

    _____

3. Are there any sentences that should be deleted from the summary? _____

4. What details are listed in the summary? _____

    _____

5. What is the title of the source?

    _____

10-4c	Using Summaries in an Annotated Bibliography

Directions: *With a partner or group, use the following annotated bibliography entry as you consider which of the below columns apply to this entry (mark an X in each box that applies); then, answer the questions at the bottom of the page.*

Gunderman, P., & Insher, Q. (2018). What does remediation do? *Modern Remediation, 23*(3), 12–31. https://doi.org/40.6709/0190074713716

The authors examine the effects of remedial and developmental education on students who required different degrees of remediation. It is noted that the inclusion of a multiple levels of unpreparedness within the study allows for the gleaning of a broader perspective of the overall impact of developmental education. Longitudinal data from Tennessee is used to accomplish the task set forth in the paper. Both two and four-year colleges and universities data for mathematics-based, reading-based and writing-based developmental and remedial courses act as the bases for the data garnered and analyzed. A regression discontinuity technique is employed to approximate results on student outcomes. In doing so, the work concludes that the effectiveness of developmental education is premised on nuanced factors that can translate into positive gains for some underprepared students and negative gains for others.

The paper provides clear support of the notion that there is no "one-size fits approach" for student success when discussing underprepared populations. The work has relevance in its multi-disciplinary approach when aggregating and disaggregating data and results. Furthermore, the authors' inclusion of "Grade in First College-Level Course" is imperative to fully foster a clear understanding as to the effect of remedial and developmental education holistically.

Evaluates the author	Compares or contrasts with other sources	Indicates how the source informs on the topic	Comments on usefulness	Provides a clear summary

1. Based on the information provided, is the summary an adequate length? If so, why?

   _____

2. Does the summary use APA format correctly?

   _____

3. From the annotation, what do you think is the topic of the research?

   _____

10-5 | Citing Your Source

Review

When you summarize, cite your source.

Include an **in-text citation** in the body of the paper and an entry in the Works Cited or References page at the end of the paper. The in-text citation directs the reader to the bibliography page. Be sure to consistently use the same citation style. Your instructor may tell you which one to use.

Understand how citation styles work.

Three common citation styles are MLA (Modern Language Association), APA (American Psychological Association), and CMS (*Chicago Manual of Style*). Each style differs slightly from the others. MLA and APA use the author's surname to link the in-text citation with the bibliography. The bibliography is organized alphabetically. In MLA, a bibliography is titled Works Cited; in APA, it's titled References.

Examples of **in-text citations**:

- MLA: Dominance hierarchies are the rule among communal animals, and pet owners must ensure they are at the top of that hierarchy (Grandin and Johnson 164).

- APA: Dominance hierarchies are the rule among communal animals, and pet owners must ensure they are at the top of that hierarchy (Grandin & Johnson, 2005, p. 164).

Examples of **bibliographic citations**:

- MLA: Grandin, Temple, and Catherine Johnson. *Animals in Translation*. Harcourt, 2005.

- APA: Grandin, T., & Johnson, C. (2005). *Animals in translation*. Harcourt.

CMS works differently. It uses a superscript number in the text to link to a list of footnotes (at the bottom of the page) or endnotes (at the end of the paper). The notes are arranged by number. CMS also allows for a comprehensive alphabetical bibliography of all the sources consulted during research.

- Example of a **CMS note number**: Dominance hierarchies are the rule among communal animals, and pet owners must ensure they are at the top of that hierarchy.[2]

- Example of a **CMS foot/endnote**: 2. Temple Grandin and Catherine Johnson, *Animals in Translation* (Orlando: Harcourt, 2005), 164.

- Example of a **CMS bibliographic entry**: Grandin, Temple, and Catherine Johnson. *Animals in Translation*. Orlando: Harcourt, 2005.

Don't include a page number in the citation if you are summarizing the entire work, a one-page work, or a work with no page numbers (such as a website).

Use a signal phrase to begin your summary.

A signal phrase uses the author's name or the work's title to introduce the summary.

Example of a **signal phrase**: In *Animals in Translation*, Temple Grandin uses her understanding …

10-5a | Citing Sources

Directions: *Answer the questions in complete sentences.*

Roberston, J. 'Event Horizons: An Analysis of Higher Education for African Americans.'
 Today's Educators, vol. 2, Spring 2017, p. 54.

This work examines, from a socio-historical perspective, the arduous trajectory undergone by African-Americans towards higher education. The author couches the context of his discussion in a historical analysis of the America's higher education system. Emancipation, Reconstruction, Federal Acts, Federal Laws and the ultimate founding of Historically Black Colleges and Universities are primary topics that are covered throughout the article. Furthermore, Duster's framing of disparities endured by African-Americans in regard to higher education is given a global correlation via international exemplars of divisive systemic measures practiced in other countries that mirror the discriminatory social norms that once were prolific in the United States. Specifically, an extensive analysis of the detrimental effects of India's caste system and South Africa's apartheid are juxtaposed to America's racial and class system.

Duster's article is relevant for developing a historical understanding of the conditions by which development education initiatives can be attributed to. Disparate conditions of disenfranchised groups yield environments that can stunt progression in many aspects for several decades that follow the cession of the practices that cause said conditions. Therefore, gaps in understanding experienced by developmental students today are, in part, a by-product of defunct social practices. Equitable access measures in higher education are necessary to avoid the practice of "systemic replication of privilege in society".

1. What citation style is the citation written in? _____

2. What page of the source is the annotation based on? _____

3. What type of source is used (i.e., book, article, website)? _____

4. Why do you cite sources? _____

_____

10-5b | Citing Sources

Directions: *Unscramble the following information for each question based on the indicated citation format (APA, MLA, or Chicago). Write a citation in the space provided.*

1. APA (website)
   From http://www.corequisitesworkbook.com/-sdc/educa/educanew.html
   April 28
   2003
   Retrieved February 2009, 6
   The Corequisite Workbook
   Robert Baldwin

2. MLA (book)
   Fantastic Ideas about Learning
   Minnie Lewis
   2002
   Print
   New Daylight Publishing

3. Chicago (periodical)
   Modern Houston Engineers
   32–41
   Magnus Walker
   "Overcoming Structural Obstacles"
   2016
   3
   December

4. APA (YouTube)
   May 16, 2013
   Understand the Brain with Medical Research [Video]
   https://www.youtube.com/watch?v=OcZ7lMfrJzQ
   YouTube
   LabTV

5. MLA (online)
   May 16, 2013
   Accessed July 6, 2018
   Blue Dolphin Publishing
   Google Book Search
   Rivers Johnson II
   www.johnsontruckingsolutions.org/planning/2018/
   Trucking in the 21st Century
   1973
   Alabama
   August 12
   Roddingham University

6. APA (magazine article)
   February 19, 2020
   https://www.wired.com/story/physicists-take-their-closest-look-yet-at-an-antimatter-atom/
   Physicists Take Their Closest Look Yet at an Antimatter Atom
   Wired
   Sophia Chen

7. MLA (book with no author)
   Alberta
   Modern Engines
   1991

8. Chicago (dissertation)
   Retrieved from http://sandwiches.che.org/stream/1973/12128/2/Hong_vpn_2336U_54321.pdf
   2014
   The art of making sandwiches (Doctoral dissertation)
   Texas Southern University
   Simon Hong

9. APA (periodical)
   Current Sociology
   68(1)
   3–21
   Sara Hanafi
   Global Sociology Revisited: Toward New Directions
   https://doi.org/10.1177/0011392119869051
   October 29, 2019

10. MLA (book chapter)
    In the Middle of the Night
    123–159
    Print
    Francis House Publishing
    Edgar Panzer
    2001
    "One More Trip"
    New York

| **10-5c** | Citing Sources |

Directions: *With a partner or group, find sources as indicated, and scramble the information needed for a citation entry. Then, exchange assignment sheets and create citation entries according to the style named. Review and discuss your responses.*

1. MLA (scholarly article with 3 authors)

    Source info:

    _____   _____

    _____   _____

    _____   _____

    Citation:

    _____

    _____

2. APA (web page with no author)

    Source info:

    _____   _____

    _____   _____

    _____   _____

    Citation:

    _____

    _____

3. MLA (book chapter)

    Source info:

    _____   _____

    _____   _____

    _____   _____

    Citation:

    _____

    _____

| **11-1** | When and Why to Quote |

Review

Quoting means repeating the exact words of your source. Using quotations skillfully in your research paper can help keep readers interested and involved.

Quote technical information if it can't be paraphrased and remain accurate.

Sometimes technical information can't be restated without changing the meaning or adding a lot of unnecessary words. If that happens, quote your source.

> Example of **quoting technical information**: Weisend (2015) defines the critical velocity "as 1/ d1/4 where D is the characteristic diameter of the flow system."

Quote when you need the exact words of an expert.

An expert may be someone who has researched the subject you're writing about or someone who has firsthand experience of it. Sometimes the expert's words are phrased so well that they will have a greater impact on your reader than a paraphrase. You may also want to fairly represent a source's stance on your topic so that you can disagree with it. In such cases, use a quotation.

- Example of **quoting an expert**: As renowned linguist David Crystal (2014) has observed, "A remarkable creativity surrounds the vocabulary of death."
- Example of **quoting a stance you disagree with**: In 1886, the German philosopher Friedrich Nietzsche characterized Beethoven as "only the final chords of a stylistic transition, a break in style" and predicted that his music would soon fall out of favor. However, a perusal of twenty-first-century concert programs provides clear evidence that Nietzsche was wrong.

Quote when you are analyzing your source's language.

Sometimes you are writing about the language used in your source. In such cases, you need to share that language with your readers. This happens, for instance, when you are writing about a historical document, a literary work, or song lyrics. In such cases, use only the most crucial and relevant ideas from the passage you want to quote. It's easier to weave shorter quotations into your sentences.

> Example of **quoting from a historical document**: In signing the Magna Carta, King John agreed to "obtaining the common counsel of the kingdom," making possible the creation of Parliament.

Limit the number of quotations you use.

Using too many quotations can make it hard for readers to recognize your ideas. Worse, it may look as if you don't have anything original to say, so quote only when you really need your source's exact words.

11-1a — When and Why to Quote

Directions: *Answer each question with a complete sentence and briefly explain your answers.*

1. Can you quote a source to provide evidence for a claim?

   _____

2. Should you use quotes for a point presented in a special format that helps to convey the intended idea to the reader?

   _____

3. When analyzing a passage, is it appropriate to use quotes?

   _____

4. If a writer is making a claim, should he use quotes if they do not support his assertion?

   _____

5. Should a quote be used in order to clarify information from the source?

   _____

6. If an unusual or infrequently used term is presented, is it acceptable to use a quote?

   _____

7. When an author is unknown, can you quote the information?

   _____

8. Is it acceptable to quote when discussing particular arguments?

   _____

9. Should a quote be used to emphasize an authoritative source?

   _____

10. Is it acceptable to quote information if it is relevant to the topic you are discussing?

   _____

11-1b | When and Why to Quote

Directions: *For each circumstance listed below, indicate whether using quotes is appropriate or not; briefly explain your answers.*

1. To re-create certain phrasing

   _____

2. If sources contain technical terms

   _____

3. To provide credibility by using experts' perspectives

   _____

4. To express relevant statements of opinion from authoritative sources

   _____

5. To present information that is being explained

   _____

6. When you do not fully understand the source

   _____

7. To add more sentences to an essay to meet a required length

   _____

8. To use your own ideas in an original writing

   _____

9. When presenting dialogue

   _____

10. When presenting evidence from the source

    _____

11-1c | When and Why to Quote

Directions: *With a partner or group, list five situations when you should use quotes in your writing and explain for each situation why quoting is necessary. Finally, provide five real-world applications where using quotes is necessary and discuss responses.*

Five situations when it is appropriate to use quotes in your writing:

1. _____

2. _____

3. _____

4. _____

5. _____

Five reasons why it is appropriate to use quotes in those situations:

1. _____

2. _____

3. _____

4. _____

5. _____

Five real-world situations that necessitate quoting:

1. _____

2. _____

3. _____

4. _____

5. _____

11-2   Introducing Quotations with Signal Phrases

Review

Use signal phrases to introduce quotations.

To introduce a quotation, you may use a phrase or you may use an entire sentence. A signal phrase or sentence usually includes the name of the writer you're quoting. It may also include a description of the writer's expertise or other background material or the title of the source of the quotation. A **signal phrase** lets your readers know why the quotation is important.

- Example of a **signal phrase**: U.S. Navy geographer Robert Biggs explained...

- Example of a **signal sentence**: The United Nations Environment Program (UNEP) studied the effects of Saddam's water policies on the Mesopotamian marshlands. In 2001, they reported...

Choose introductory verbs carefully.

The verb you use to introduce a quotation tells readers what you think of the source's ideas. Do you believe the source is trustworthy? Do you doubt the source's accuracy? Do you agree or disagree with the source? The verb you choose indicates your opinion.
For instance, the verb *allege* indicates you may not trust the source's words.

> Example of a **verb implying doubt**: In its defense, the company alleged the plaintiffs had come into contact with the toxin through "negligent handling."

When you choose a verb, pay careful attention to the impression your word choice will convey to your readers. Verbs that may give a negative impression include *allege, claim, imagine,* and *suppose.* Verbs that imply your source is trustworthy include *explain, find, recount,* and *report.* Neutral verbs include *believe, propose, say,* and *state.*

Use the verb tense preferred by your citation style.

You also need to think about which tense of the verb to use. This often depends on the documentation style your instructor wants you to follow. MLA prefers present tense verbs (no matter how old the source is), while APA prefers past tense verbs.

- Example of **present tense verb in a signal phrase** (MLA): In *Antigone*, Choragos voices one of the Sophocles's themes when he comments, "The inflexible heart breaks first, the toughest iron / Cracks first, and the wildest horses bend their necks / At the pull of the smallest curb" (lines 377–379).
- Example of a **past tense verb in a signal phrase** (APA): Djoussé and his colleagues (2009) found that eating one or more eggs a day "is associated with an increased risk of type 2 diabetes in both men and women" (p. 219).

CMS style accepts both tenses and advises integrating the tense in the signal phrase into the tense of your paper as a whole.

11-2a	Introducing Quotations with Signal Phrases

Directions: *Fill in the blanks with quotes of your own invention to form complete sentences that use quotations.*

1. From the beginning, "_____."

2. _____ says, "_____."

3. In the work, _____ states, "_____."

4. According to _____, "_____."

5. As noted in _____ Journal, "_____";

    however, _____ believes "_____."

6. _____ writes "_____."

7. Even though _____ feels that "_____", he
    actually writes, "_____."

8. Based on _____ own words, "_____."

9. The famous singer always says, "_____."

10. At the end of every class session, Professor _____ reminds students
    that "_____."

11. The UFO skeptic feels that aliens are _____, but the federal report
    reads "_____."

12. When in doubt about _____, Mr. Jones tells the students to
    "_____."

13. While reading the book, he heard someone scream, "_____."

14. Since he knows the format, the manager told him, "_____."

15. The college advisor made sure to tell the returning student that "_____
    _____."

11-2b   Introducing Quotations with Signal Phrases

Directions: *For each of the below quotes, write an appropriate signal phrase in the space provided.*

1. _____, "The car was found at the corner of Live Oak and Cleburne."

2. _____, "Can the storm get any worse than it was last year?"

3. _____, "video games have advanced quite bit over the last decade"; however, _____, "even more advances are to come in the next two years."

4. _____, "Please stop calling my phone after 6 p.m."

5. _____, "unfortunately, he still wants to keep the dog."

6. Since the beginning of the semester, _____, "you need to come to class on time or you'll probably fail the tests."

7. Besides being an instructor, Bob Akin is also _____, "new movies need more classically trained actors like in the past."

8. In the comic book, _____, "Stop there, you villain!"

9. _____, "Please help me," but no one stopped.

10. Before the end of summer, _____, "we really need to visit the beach."

11. _____, "Just cut a little off the top."

12. No longer a fan for the home team, _____, "I'm not going to buy season tickets ever again in my life."

13. _____, "you gave it your best try, so be proud."

14. As the waiter approached our table, _____, "I really wish you had come five minutes ago when I was hungry."

15. _____, "I worked there before the management changed, back in 2016."

11-2c | Introducing Quotations with Signal Phrases

Directions: *With a partner or group, use the signal phrases shown in parentheses and create sentences that introduce or integrate quotations. Add punctuation correctly.*

1. (According to)

   _____

2. (By the end)

   _____

3. (At the start)

   _____

4. (After the fight)

   _____

5. (Claims the coach)

   _____

6. (Writes Nurse Tegwi)

   _____

7. (Advises Betty Fortune)

   _____

8. (Warns the CDC)

   _____

9. (Points out that)

   _____

10. (Melba Martin notes)

    _____

11. (Rachel Marcus laughs)

    _____

12. (Jacki Nunez believes)

    _____

11-3 | Embedding Quotations in Your Sentences

Review

Quotations should be woven into the flow of your paper so that it reads naturally. Introduce them in a way that helps readers understand why you selected those passages.

Indicate the source's authority and value.

The language you use to embed a quotation should tell readers why they your source is credible and worthy of their attention. You can do this by indicating traits of the person you're quoting, such as occupation, position, knowledge, and experience.

> Example of **establishing a source's credibility**: John Bischof, the lead researcher on the team that made the breakthrough, stressed that their discovery "could have a huge societal benefit if we could someday bank organs for transplant" (as quoted in University of Minnesota, 2013, para. 10).

Quote only what's needed.

If a quotation is too long or too detailed, you run the risk of losing your reader's attention. You can trim a longer quotation in order to use only the most relevant portions. When you do this, use ellipses (…) to stand in for missing words.

> Example of **using ellipses**: Known as the father of psychoanalysis, Sigmund Freud began his 1899 book *The Interpretation of Dreams* by stating his intention to "demonstrate that there is a psychological technique which makes it possible to interpret dreams, … to elucidate the processes which underlie the strangeness and obscurity of dreams, and to deduce from these processes the nature of the psychic forces whose conflict or cooperation is responsible for our dreams" (3).

Analyze your quotation.

After the quotation, write at least one sentence explaining how the quotation relates to your ideas. It may:

- provide an example of the point you're making,
- introduce a different perspective that you plan to explore, or
- serve as a counterargument that you'll refute so that your own argument is more convincing.

In the example below, the quotation sums up what has become accepted opinion about Freud's dream theory, and the analysis introduces evidence that will refute it, at least in part.

> Example of **analyzing a quotation**: After reviewing the research in dream theory done in the latter half of the 20th century, Bill Domhoff (2000) of the University of California concluded that there is "nothing … explicitly 'Freudian' … except that at least some dreams have psychological meaning" (p. 652). However, more recent research has suggested Freud may have been right in viewing dreams as a way of coming to grips with suppressed thoughts.

| **11-3a** | Embedding Quotations in Your Sentences |

Directions: *Write sentences that include the following statement and quotation in four different passages: practice embedding the quote at the beginning of the passage, in the middle, and at the end of a passage.*

Sanaa wants to run track for the varsity team since she is tall and fast. However, she lacks stamina and refuses to practice with anyone besides her coaches at school to improve.

Quote: "Running is an endurance sport that requires being open to learn from anyone. A true runner must focus on what's ahead and not look behind. So, running demands mental fortitude and dedication" (Wintz 122).

Embed at the start:

_____

_____

_____

Embed in the middle:

_____

_____

_____

Embed at the end:

_____

_____

_____

Embed throughout the passage:

_____

_____

_____

11-3b | Embedding Quotations in Your Sentences

Directions: *For each entry below, write a sentence that embeds the quotation, using the signal verb or phrase provided.*

1. Signal verb: Demonstrates

    Quote: "Students who study perform better on exams than those who do not."

    _____

2. Signal verb: Argues

    Quote: "Digital downloads are much better than cassette tapes."

    _____

3. Signal verb: Explains

    Quote: "At the current rate, not enough students will enroll by the fall semester."

    _____

4. Signal verb: Writes

    Quote: "Without more resources, the free lunch program will end later this month."

    _____

5. Signal verb: Asserts

    Quote: "Laser disc players were not well received by the public."

    _____

6. Signal phrase: Based on data

    Quote: "Fewer people are opting to buy homes through traditional financing programs."

    _____

7. Signal verb: Clarifies

    Quote: "The layoffs will not include the faculty and staff."

    _____

11-3c   Embedding Quotations in Your Sentences

Directions: *With a partner or group, write five quotes in the space indicated. Then, exchange worksheets and, in the "Sentences" section below, write a sentence for each quote that embeds the quote in the location indicated, using the provided signal verb or phrase. Discuss your responses.*

Quotes

1. _____

2. _____

3. _____

4. _____

5. _____

Sentences

1. Location: *In the middle*   Signal verb: Explains

   _____

   _____

2. Location: *At the end*   Signal verb: Asserts

   _____

   _____

3. Location: *At the start*   Signal phrase: According to

   _____

   _____

4. Location: *In the middle*   Signal verb: Comments

   _____

   _____

5. Location: *At the start*   Signal phrase: From the start,

   _____

   _____

11-4   Block Quotations

Review

Follow your citation style rules to determine when to use a block quotation.

Your instructor has probably told you which citation style to use. Guidelines differ from style to style.

- MLA requires a block format for prose quotations that take more than four lines of your page.
- APA requires a block format if the quotation is more than 40 words long.
- CMS requires a block format if the quotation is 100 words or longer or if it is longer than one paragraph.

Indent block quotations half an inch from the left margin.

A block quotation does not need to be enclosed in quotation marks. Instead, to show that the passage is quoted material (and not your own words), it is indented half an inch from the left margin.

Introduce and end a block quotation clearly.

Many writers introduce a block quotation with a complete sentence followed by a colon. If your signal phrase does not form a complete sentence, it may be followed by a comma or by no punctuation at all. In MLA or APA, end the block quotation by placing the in-text citation after—not before—the final punctuation.

Use only the most relevant parts of the quoted material.

Even though you're quoting several sentences or even paragraphs, you must still make sure you're not including words that are not needed. When you leave out words, phrases, or even sentences, use an ellipsis (…) to indicate some part is missing.

If necessary, change the quotation to make it clear and grammatically correct.

The quoted material may include a pronoun that is not defined in that passage, or removing unnecessary portions may result in ungrammatical constructions. In these cases, use brackets to indicate that words have been added or changed.

> Example of a **block quotation**: In his *Second Treatise on Government*, philosopher John Locke (1764) made a cogent case for majority rule:
>
> > Sect. 97. And thus, every man, by consenting with others to make one body politic under one government, puts himself under an obligation, to every one of that society, to submit to the determination of the majority, and to be concluded by it [;] (Chapter III)

11-4a	Block Quotations

Directions: *Indicate whether each quote meets the criteria to be treated as a block quotation; in MLA style if it does, correctly write and punctuate a block quotation in the space provided. In Part III, briefly explain your decisions.*

I. Source: unknown

Quote: "The man loves to eat candy and hamburgers every Friday with his daughter at her school."

Acceptable _____   Not Acceptable _____

_____

_____

_____

_____

II. Source: Finglestein, Nicholas. *Community College.* Education Books, 2018, 24.

Quote: "Regarding size, populations served and community needs, urban and rural community colleges may experience some contrasts. Urban community colleges tend to be larger in size (campuses, buildings, etc....) when compared to rural community colleges. The feasible reason for the size differential is population size. Urban areas tend to have larger populations than do rural ones. Therefore, their respective community college sizes reflect population size. Furthermore, populations between urban and rural community colleges also differ."

Acceptable _____   Not Acceptable _____

_____

_____

_____

_____

III. _____

_____

_____

_____

11-4b | Block Quotations

Directions: *Answer the questions in complete sentences.*

1. What is a block quotation?

   _____

2. Is it appropriate to treat a 10-word sentence as a block quotation?

   _____

3. In MLA style, when should block quotations be used?

   _____

4. Do block quotations require quotation marks?

   _____

5. When using a block quotation, should you include the page number of the source?

   _____

6. Should block quotations be single-spaced?

   _____

7. Is an introduction to the block quote required?

   _____

8. When using a block quotation, should you explain why you used it in your text following the quotation?

   _____

9. Is it appropriate to treat a short passage or summary as a block quotation?

   _____

10. Is it acceptable to use a block quotation when you need only a small portion of a quote?

    _____

11-4c | Block Quotations

Directions: *With a partner or group, complete Part I by finding or creating three quotes of different lengths. Exchange worksheets and, in Part II, indicate whether each of the quotes from Part I meets the criteria for a block quote. Discuss responses.* (Note: The criterion for setting a quotation as a block is based on typewritten lines, but for the purposes of this worksheet, you may substitute the number of handwritten lines instead.)

Part I

1. Quote:

   _____

   _____

   _____

   _____

2. Quote:

   _____

   _____

   _____

   _____

3. Quote:

   _____

   _____

   _____

   _____

Part II

1. Explanation:

   _____

2. Explanation:

   _____

3. Explanation:

   _____

11-5 | Citing Quotations

Review

Cite each quotation.

Every time you include a quotation in your paper, you need to indicate where the original quotation can be found. You do this by including an in-text citation (MLA or APA) or note number (CMS). Your reader can use this citation or note number to find the complete citation entry on the Works Cited or References page or in the foot- or endnotes.

Follow the formatting guidelines of your citation style.

In MLA style, include the author's last name and page number in parentheses at the end of the quotation. You might also include the author's name or source title in a signal phrase that introduces the quotation. If no author is named, include the first several words of the title. Place the end punctuation after the closing parenthesis.

> Example of an **in-text citation (MLA)**: The title of Faulkner's novel alludes to a Bible verse in which King David mourns the death of his estranged and rebellious son: "And the king was much moved, and went up to the chamber over the gate, and wept: and as he went, thus he said, O my son Absalom, my son, my son Absalom! would God I had died for thee, O Absalom, my son, my son!" (*King James Version*, 2 Sam. 18.33).

In APA style, include the author's last name, year of publication and page number. Use the abbreviation p-period (p.) for page or pp-period (pp.) for pages. If you're citing a source without page numbers, you can use the abbreviation para-period (para.) to signal which paragraph you cited. You can include all three elements in parentheses at the end of the quotation. Or you can include the author's name and date in a signal phrase that introduces the quotation. Place the end punctuation after the closing parenthesis.

> Example of an **in-text citation (APA)**: NASA (2013), which is the U.S. government agency responsible for aerospace research and the country's nonmilitary space program, warned that over half a million pieces of space debris—including "nonfunctional spacecraft, abandoned launch vehicle stages, mission-related debris, and fragmentation debris" (para. 5)—are orbiting Earth at speeds as great as 17,500 mph.

In *Chicago* style, place a superscript, or raised number, after the end punctuation. This number refers the reader to the relevant foot- or endnote.

> Example of an **in-text citation (CMS)**: Seventeenth-century political philosopher and author of *Leviathan* Thomas Hobbes was among "the earliest western philosophers to count women as persons when devising a social contract."[4]

> Example of a **foot-/endnote (CMS)**: 4. Sharon A. Lloyd and Susanne Sreedhar, "Hobbes's Moral and Political Philosophy," Stanford Encyclopedia of Philosophy, last modified April 30, 2018, https://plato.stanford.edu/entries/hobbes-moral/.

| **11-5a** | Citing Quotations |

Directions: *For each quotation below, create an intext citation based on the type of source indicated and in the style indicated. Add all additional information needed to create each citation.*

1. MLA (print scholarly journal)

    "The vitality of the program lies in its ability to sustain itself during times of budgetary crisis."

    _____

2. APA (newspaper)

    "The probability of the car lasting for more than two years is slim. It will more than likely break down for good in a month or so."

    _____

3. MLA (YouTube video)

    "Nexcsa Sweet Tea is an organic product that is well worth its high cost."

    _____

4. Chicago (database journal)

    "Fluctuations in local economics lead to various distressing trends. For example, crime rates are increasing at a steady pace while home ownership is decreasing significantly. If this situation continues, the city will face a long-term crisis."

    _____

5. MLA (online scholarly journal)

    "I will facilitate monthly meetings to help develop plans for the corequisite program."

    _____

6. Chicago (web page)

    "The new improvements to the operational structure have paid off. Productivity has increased and profits are steady."

    _____

11-5b | Citing Quotations

Directions: *Correctly cite each quotation in the citation style specified, based on the information provided.*

I.

MLA style

Quote:

"The maturation process is complex, but necessary for student development and purposeful engagement in learning. Being that Dixon's Theory is based on the work of Tsui in a modified iteration, the order of development is emphasized as a key factor in a student's ability to develop. However, one ancillary pitfall of the process is the possible creation of psychosocial dissonance." (page 43, Henderson, X. (2013). 113 New York NY, 2007 Maturation.)

II.

APA style

Quote:

"The community needs for urban community colleges and rural community colleges also diverge at times. Just as institutional size and populations, community needs also dictate the composition of a community college. For example, in an urban setting that houses a wide variety of industry with variances in employment opportunities, there is an opportunity to offer a wide variety of programs to meet these implied and expressed needs of industry. On the other hand, many rural areas are not as expansive in employment opportunities to help sustain a community. Therefore, rural community college course offerings may be fewer and narrower in scope than those of urban community colleges (page 234, Breyia Walker, 2016)"

11-5c | Citing Quotations

Directions: *Using the information provided, create APA-style entries for a works cited page.*

1. 2008. Marx, Q. L., & Tran, T. The model student. *Model students* (2nd ed.). Goodnight Publishing.

    _____

2. (1976). Two years as a professor. 23–41 *Modern professors*, Jones, V.J. 2(3).

    _____

3. Better tomorrow. *New Teaching Methods*, https://doi.org/12.1346/t1288-4423(89)11012-2, Henry, L., & Quintin, P. (2009). *23*(1), 102–129.

    _____

4. Humphrey-Jones. Benjamin, A., & Lightfoot, M. (2003). *Leaders: A strategic guide* (4th ed.).

    _____

5. Texas Southern Business School Press. (1999). *Super ideas: 21ˢᵗ century instruction.* Gin, W., & Straub, T.

    _____

6. J. M. Qualls (1963). Miller & Associates. *Foundations.*

    _____

7. Learning to learn. *Journal of Learning, 12*(3), 133–145. Wells, D., Jasmin, R., Phillips, A., Smith, E., Roberts, J., & Raju, R. (2001).

    _____

8. (1992). *Remediation Journal, 21*(2), 342–413. Scott, T., Braxton, D., Loving, N., & Spencer, F. Changes in remediation practices: A new approach.

    _____

12-1　Identifying Sources and Their Publication Information

Review

To cite a source properly, you first need to know what type of publication it is. It may be a book, a periodical, or a website.

Use the author, title, publisher, and date to cite a book.

You can find most of the information you need to cite a book on the title page. If any of the details are missing, look for them on the copyright page, which is on the back of the title page. There may be several publication dates. If there are, choose the most recent.

>Example of an **MLA book citation**:
>Zinsser, William. *On Writing Well*. Collins, 2006.

If you only need to cite an article in a book, find the title and author in the table of contents. Then find the page range; you'll need the page range in your citation.

>Example of an **MLA citation for an article in a book**:
>Doss, Erika. "The Art of Cultural Politics: From Regionalism to Abstract Expressionism." *Recasting America: Culture and Politics in the Age of Cold War*, edited by Lary May, U of Chicago P, 1988, pp. 195–220.

Use the author, article title, periodical name, date, and page numbers to cite an article in a periodical.

Newspapers, popular magazines, and scholarly journals are each documented differently. If you used a database to find the article, you may be able to find an online citation, but you will need to reformat it depending on the citation style your instructor wants you to use.

>Example of an **APA citation for a newspaper article**:
>Fadroski, K. (2018, July 22). Sleep through this. *Los Angeles Daily News*, C1, C3.

Use the author, article title, website title, publisher, publication date, access date, and DOI or URL to cite a website.

Finding the information you need on a website is not always easy. If you can't find the individual or corporate author on the same page as the article, look at these pages: *Home*, *About*, *Biography*, or *Contact*. If there's no author, start your citation with the title of the article or webpage.

>Example of a **Chicago Style citation for an article on a website**:
>"Spinal Cord Injury: Hope Through Research," National Institutes of Health, last modified August 8, 2018. https://www.ninds.nih.gov/Disorders/Patient-Caregiver -Education/Hope-Through-Research/Spinal-Cord-Injury-Hope-Through-Research.

12-1a	Identifying Sources and Their Publication Information

Directions: *Answer the questions in complete sentences.*

1. Quote: Most of these [ESL] students' issues are related to contextual understanding, not gaps in learning (Morris, 2013).

    Based on the above citation, whose ideas are being paraphrased in the quote? _____

2. McWane, D. (2012). *Learning*. Jackson-Hill.

    If this is formatted in APA style; what type of source is being cited? _____

3. Jones, O., & Rose, B. (2013). The modern college instructor. *Leading the charge* (2nd ed.). Sanchez.

    In the above citation entry, who is the publisher? _____

4. Reading is an essential, but overlooked, skill necessary for college success (Stagg, 2002, p.15).

    What page(s) does the quote come from? _____

5. Texas Department of Developmental Studies. (2018). *Ohio Education*. Gunther.

    What is the title of the work? _____

6. Ramey, E. (1991).

    Assume the above citation is intended to be an entry for an APA-style cite of a book with more than one author. What is missing from the entry? _____

7. Smith, F. (1992). A study of the effects of sleep deprivation. *Journal of Sleeping*, 9(3), 11–16. http://www.workbookexamples.com/full/url/

    Who is the author of the above article? _____

8. "According to the president, 'no more money is in the budget,'" says Dr. Muntz (King, 2003).

    Who wrote the work where the quote is located? _____

9. Johnson, Oscar, & Rosenthal, B. (2013). The Modern Math Guide. Business Math (2nd ed.). Julius.

    Are there any errors in the above citation (formatted in APA style)? _____

10. "The program requires more analytical data to be effective" (Pilzner, 2009, p. 34).

    In the citation above, can you determine the year of publication? If so, what is it? _____

12-1b | Identifying Sources and Their Publication Information

Directions: *Read the following material and answer the questions as indicated.*

I.

> The maturation process is complex, but it is necessary for student development and purposeful engagement in learning. Being that Dixon's Theory is based on the work of Tsui in a modified iteration, the order of development is emphasized as a key factor in a student's ability to develop. However, one ancillary pitfall of the process is the possible creation of psychosocial dissonance (Henderson, 2013).
>
> Source: Henderson, X. (2013). *Maturation*. Broom-Mountain.
>
> 1) Who is the author of the source?
>   _____
>
> 2) Who is the publisher?
>   _____
>
> 3) What is the year of publication?
>   _____
>
> 4) What is the title of the source?
>   _____

> The concept of acceleration as a best practice is reiterated throughout current literature pertaining to developmental education, and this paper does a good job in framing a coherent discussion on the topic that is outcome specific. As an exploratory practice to generate higher levels of student success within developmental courses, accelerated models of remediation may offer a viable means to achieve this goal. The work provides recommendations for doable practices that can be modified to an institution's needs. This, it is a good beginning resource for researching corequisite remediation.
>
> Source: Rixby, Audrey, and Felix Jackson. "Accelerated Models Best Practices," *New Developmental Education Reforms*, vol. 2, pp. 23–31.
>
> 5) Who is the author of the source?
>   _____
>
> 6) What is the volume?
>   _____
>
> 7) What is the year of publication?
>   _____

12-1c	Identifying Sources and Their Publication Information

Directions: *With a partner or group, write three MLA-style citations in the numbered spaces. Exchange worksheets and fill in the required information for each entry, as indicated.*

1. _____

   _____

   Author(s): _____

   Title: _____

   Date: _____

   City: _____

   Publisher: _____

   Page(s): _____

   Url: _____

   Website: _____

2. _____

   _____

   Author(s): _____

   Title: _____

   Date: _____

   City: _____

   Publisher: _____

   Page(s): _____

   Url: _____

   Website: _____

12-2	The Basics of Documentation

Review

Documenting your sources helps establish your credibility. Documentation involves two elements: an in-text citation and a bibliography page.

Use in-text citations in the body of your paper.

Whenever you quote, paraphrase, or summarize material from your research, document the source in your paper using an **in-text citation**. This is a short citation that points readers to a complete citation on your bibliography page.

Examples of **in-text citations:**

- MLA: Dominance hierarchies are the rule among communal animals, and pet owners must ensure they are at the top of that hierarchy (Grandin and Johnson 164).
- APA: Dominance hierarchies are the rule among communal animals, and pet owners must ensure they are at the top of that hierarchy (Grandin & Johnson, 2005, p. 164).

Examples of **bibliographic citations**:

- MLA: Grandin, Temple, and Catherine Johnson. *Animals in Translation*. Harcourt, 2005.
- APA: Grandin, T., & Johnson, C. (2005). *Animals in translation*. Orlando, FL: Harcourt.

Three citation formats are commonly used: Modern Language Association (MLA), American Psychological Association (APA), and *Chicago Manual of Style* (CMS).

Create a separate bibliography page.

The bibliography page lists your sources and gives full bibliographic information about each. No matter which citation style you're using—usually MLA, APA, or CMS—your bibliography will provide information about your sources such as author, title, publisher, and date of publication. If relevant, it will include other information, too, such as the editor, translator, and URL. When using MLA, title your bibliography a Works Cited page; when using APA, title your bibliography page References. CMS titles this page Bibliography.

   If your readers need to find the sources you used, your bibliography allows them to do so.

12-2a	The Basics of Documentation

Directions: *Answer the questions clearly and completely.*

1. What are the three primary citation formats?

   _____

2. What is a works-cited page?

   _____

3. What is a citation?

   _____

4. What are three basic elements of a citation?

   _____

5. What is a parenthetical reference?

   _____

6. What is an annotated bibliography?

   _____

7. What material should be documented (cited)?

   _____

8. What is a block quote?

   _____

9. What is paraphrasing and should it be cited?

   _____

10. Is the following sentence documented correctly, in APA format?

    Anjana and Rachel sometimes say, "The procedures are in place to help students succeed" (Jones, 1986, p. 232).

    _____

11. When citing an Internet source, is it necessary to always include the web address?

    _____

12. What is an in-text citation?

    _____

12-2b | The Basics of Documentation

Directions: *Answer each question in a complete sentence.*

1. What does MLA stand for?

_____

2. What does APA stand for?

_____

3. What does CMS stand for?

_____

4. Why are there different documentation (citation) formats?

_____

5. Which citation style is used in most English courses?

_____

6. What is an embedded quote?

_____

7. Do embedded quotes require documentation (citation)?

_____

8. What is the difference between a works-cited page and a bibliography?

_____

9. When do you not need documentation (citation)?

_____

10. What spacing is required in MLA and APA documentations (citations)?

_____

11. In all citation styles, is the author(s)' name included in the citation?

_____

12. What is a hanging indention? Is it required when using APA or MLA citations?

_____

12-2c The Basics of Documentation

Directions: *With a partner or group, answer the following questions as indicated.*

In MLA style:

1. How do you document a book chapter?

    _____

2. How do you document an article from a database?

    _____

3. How do you document a website?

    _____

In APA style:

4. How do you document a chapter from a printed book?

    _____

5. How do you document an article from a database?

    _____

6. How do you document a website?

    _____

In Chicago style:

1. How do you document a book chapter?

    _____

2. How do you document an article from an online database?

    _____

3. How do you document a website?

    _____

12-3 | Using MLA Format

Review

Before writing a research paper, check with your instructors to see what citation format they require, and use the most recent version available. The documentation format used primarily by literature scholars is MLA, or Modern Language Association. It also widely accepted in the arts and humanities.

Use an in-text citation whenever you quote, paraphrase, or summarize a source.

The in-text citation includes the last name of the author and the number of the page where the information is found. Place the name and page number in parentheses at the end of the source material.

> Example of an **MLA in-text citation**: At the start of seven-day-long battle of Chancellorsville, Union general Joseph Hooker was overconfident of victory, boasting that "The Confederate Army … is now the legitimate property of the Army of the Potomac" (Long and Wright 250).

There are several exceptions to this rule. If there is no named author, use the first few words of the title in quotation marks. If you have already used the author's name or the title in a signal phrase introducing the source material, only the page number needs to appear in the parenthetical citation. Some sources, notably web pages, do not have page numbers; in such cases, introduce the quotation with the author's name, and omit the parenthetical citation.

> Example of an **MLA in-text citation (no named author)**: Henry Fleming's first real experience of battle came at Chancellorsville ("The Battle").

> Example of an **MLA in-text citation (with signal phrase)**: Before Stephen Crane's young protagonist enlists in the Union Army, he imagines the battles: "They might not be distinctly Homeric, but there seemed to be much glory in them" (6).

> Example of an **MLA in-text citation (web page)**: According to the American Battlefield Trust, Union troops outnumbered Confederate troops at Chancellorsville by roughly 40,000 men.

Create a separate Works Cited page.

On the Works Cited page, list all the sources cited in your paper in alphabetical order. Alphabetize by the last name of the author or the first significant word in the title.

> Example of a **Works Cited entry**

> "The Battle: Chancellorsville." *The Red Badge of Courage*. American Studies at the U of Virginia, http://xroads.virginia.edu/~HYPER/CRANE/chancellorsville/section2.html. Accessed 17 Sept. 2018.

12-3a | Using MLA Format

Directions: *Answer the following questions as indicated.*

1. What information is included in a basic citation in MLA style?

   a. _____

   b. _____

   c. _____

   d. _____

   e. _____

2. Is a works-cited page typed on a new page with a page number? _____

3. Are the following citations correctly formatted in MLA style? If not, correct them.

   a. Document published on a website:
      United Teachers for Change. 23 Jan. 2018. Jones, Everret. http://www.4morechanges.com

      _____

   b. Article in a scholarly journal:
      Barry Middleston. *New Hope vol* 12. No. 7. (2009). "Yesterday's News." 32–45.

      _____

   c. Article in a newspaper:
      Harrisburg Press. (2006). Kreig, Elaine. "Helping Our Students." 14 June 1999, natl. ed.: R12.

      _____

4. What is the format for an MLA heading?

   _____

5. What type size does MLA style require? _____

6. How are titles of short works formatted? _____

7. How are titles of long works formatted? _____

8. You must cite when:

   _____

   _____

9. In what order are works-cited sources listed? _____

12-3b | Using MLA Format

Directions: *Answer each question in a complete sentence.*

1. When citing publication information, do you include the name of the city if the book was published after 1900?

   _____

2. What punctuation mark goes between the city and publisher in a book published before 1900?

   _____

3. What is the suggested font and type size?

   _____

4. How should a paraphrase be cited if the source is electronic and not stated in the introductory phrase?

   _____

5. How is August 13, 2017 cited?

   _____

6. Must the URL be included in a source from the Internet?

   _____

7. When a source does not have an author, how do you format an in-text citation?

   _____

8. Where in a document is a works-cited page located?

   _____

9. How do you format authors' names in a works-cited entry?

   _____

10. Is the following quote punctuated correctly? If not, correctly cite.
    "Prior to 1987, most of the city was not diversely populated". (12, Hilsburgh)

    _____

11. What words should be capitalized in a citation title?

    _____

12. Do you provide the volume and issue numbers for magazines?

    _____

12-3c | Using MLA Format

Directions: *With a partner or group, write a citation for each of the specified source types on a separate sheet. Then, for each citation, scramble the order of information, and write the scrambled elements in the spaces provided below. Exchange worksheets with your partner or another group, and write the correct citations, in MLA format, in the spaces indicated. Discuss your responses.*

1. Website:

   _____

   _____

   _____

   _____

   _____

   Citation: _____

2. Article from scholarly journal (online):

   _____

   _____

   _____

   _____

   _____

   Citation: _____

3. Book with multiple authors:

   _____

   _____

   _____

   _____

   _____

   Citation: _____

12-4	Using APA Format

Review

Before writing a research paper, check with your instructors to see what citation format they require, and use the most recent version available. The documentation format most used in the social and behavioral sciences is APA, or American Psychological Association. It is widely accepted in other fields, from business to nursing.

Use an in-text citation whenever you quote, paraphrase, or summarize a source.

The **in-text citation** includes the last name of the author, the publication date (usually the year), and, if you are quoting or paraphrasing the source, the number of the page where the information is found. Place the in-text citation in parentheses directly after your quotation, paraphrase, or summary.

> Example of an **APA in-text citation**: At the start of seven-day-long battle of Chancellorsville, Union general Joseph Hooker was overconfident of victory, boasting that "The Confederate Army … is now the legitimate property of the Army of the Potomac" (Long & Wright, 1887, p. 250).

Note that APA in-text citations commonly mention the author's name in a signal phrase followed by the date of publication in parentheses. A signal phrase uses a few words—for instance, *according to* or *as observed by*—to introduce the author and source material.

> Example of an **APA in-text citation (with signal phrase)**: Before Stephen Crane's (1896) young protagonist enlisted in the Union Army, he had a literary conception of what the battles must be like: "They might not be distinctly Homeric, but there seemed to be much glory in them" (p. 6).

If there is no named author, use the title (or a shortened version of the title).

> Example of an **APA in-text citation (no named author)**: Henry Fleming's first real experience of battle came at Chancellorsville ("The Battle").

Create a separate References page.

On the References page, list all the sources cited in your paper in alphabetical order. Alphabetize by the last name of the author. If the source doesn't have a named author, alphabetize by the first significant word in the title.

> Example of a **References entry:**
>
> The battle: Chancellorsville. *The red badge of courage*. American Studies at the University of Virginia. http://xroads.virginia.edu/~HYPER/CRANE/chancellorsville/section2.html

12-4a | Using APA Format

Directions: *Answer the following questions as indicated.*

1. What information is included in a basic citation in APA style?

   a. _____

   b. _____

   c. _____

   d. _____

   e. _____

2. Is a references page typed on a new page with a page number? _____

3. Are the following citations correctly formatted in APA style? If not, correct them.

   a. Website:

   United Teachers for Change. 23 Jan. 2018. Jones, Everret. http://www.4morechanges.com

   _____

   b. Scholarly journal:

   Barry Middleston. *New Hope vol* 12. No. 7. (2009). "Yesterday's News." 32–45.

   _____

   c. Newspaper:

   Harrisburg Press. (2006). Kreig, Elaine. "Helping Our Students." 14 June 1999, natl. ed.: R12.

   _____

4. What is the format for an APA heading? _____

5. What type size does APA require? _____

6. What is the format for an in-text citation, in APA style? _____

7. How are titles of short works formatted? _____

8. How are titles of long works formatted? _____

9. You must cite when:

   _____

   _____

10. How are references' sources ordered, in the References list? _____

12-4b | Using APA Format

Directions: *Answer each question in a complete sentence.*

1. What information appears within a running header in APA style?

   _____

2. Where is the year of publication listed in an APA citation?

   _____

3. How is the year of publication shown?

   _____

4. Should papers written in APA style be double-spaced?

   _____

5. What is the preferred font and type size?

   _____

6. What word(s) in the title of the source are capitalized?

   _____

7. What information is required to cite an article obtained from a database?

   _____

8. Is the following entry formatted correctly? If not, correctly format.
   Johnson, Albert, and Richards, Leo. 1999. *Education and identity*. Douglass Publishing.

   _____

9. Is the following in-text citation treated correctly? If not, correctly cite.
   A new study shows that "a large number of students plan to enter in the healthcare field" (Singh, 1997).

   _____

10. Should all lines of reference entries in the References list be aligned flush left?

    _____

| **12-4c** | Using APA Format |

Directions: *With a partner or group, write a citation for each of the specified source types on a separate sheet. Then, for each citation, scramble the order of information, and write the scrambled elements in the spaces provided below. Exchange worksheets with your partner or another group and write the correct citations, in APA format, in the spaces indicated below. Discuss your responses.*

1. Website:

   _____

   _____

   _____

   _____

   _____

Citation: _____

2. Article from scholarly journal (online):

   _____

   _____

   _____

   _____

   _____

Citation: _____

3. Book with multiple authors:

   _____

   _____

   _____

   _____

   _____

Citation: _____

12-5 | Using Chicago Style Format

Review

Before writing a research paper, check with your instructors to see what citation format they require, and use the most recent version available. CMS, or *The Chicago Manual of Style*, acknowledges several documentation styles. One is used in many of the humanities, such as history, philosophy, and the arts.

Identify a quote, paraphrase, or summary with a superscript number.

The superscript number is a form of **in-text citation** that directs readers to a list of notes at the foot of the page or end of the paper. This corresponds to a list of sources called the Bibliography, which includes sources cited in the paper, along with sources used to conduct research.

> Example of a **CMS note number**: Before Stephen Crane's young protagonist enlists in the Union Army, he imagines the battles: "They might not be distinctly Homeric, but there seemed to be much glory in them."[1]

The first time you cite from a source, provide a foot- or endnote including the author's full name, the title of the source, publication information (location, publisher, and date), and page number. The next time you cite the same source, list only the author's last name, the title, and the page number. Begin each note with the note number in regular font (not superscript).

> Examples of **CMS foot-/endnotes**:
>
> 1. Stephen Crane, *The Red Badge of Courage: An Episode of the American Civil War* (New York: Appleton, 1896), 6.
> 2. "The Battle: Chancellorsville," American Studies at the University of Virginia, accessed September 17, 2018. http://xroads.virginia.edu/~HYPER/CRANE/chancellorsville/section2.html.
> 3. Crane, *The Red Badge of Courage*, 58.

List your footnotes or endnotes in numerical order.

Create a separate bibliography (optional).

CMS does not require a bibliography, but your instructor may. In the bibliography, list all your research sources in alphabetical order. Alphabetize by the last name of the author. If the source doesn't have a named author, alphabetize by the first significant word in the title.

> Example of **CMS bibliography entries**:
>
> "The Battle: Chancellorsville." American Studies at the University of Virginia. Accessed September 17, 2018. http://xroads.virginia.edu/~HYPER/CRANE/chancellorsville/section2.html.
>
> "Chancellorsville." American Battlefield Trust. Accessed September 17, 2018. https://www.battlefields.org/learn/civil-war/battles/chancellorsville.

| 12-5a | Using Chicago Style Format |

Directions: *Answer the following questions as indicated.*

1. What information is included in a basic citation in *Chicago* style?

    a. _____

    b. _____

    c. _____

    d. _____

    e. _____

2. Is a works-cited page typed on a new page with a page number? _____

3. Are the following citations correctly formatted in *Chicago* style? If not, correct them.

    a.   Website:

    United Teachers for Change. 23 Jan. 2018. Jones, Everret. http://www.4morechanges.com

    _____

    b.   Scholarly journal:

    Barry Middleston. *New Hope vol* 12. No. 7. (2009). "Yesterday's News." 32–45.

    _____

    c.   Newspaper:

    Harrisburg Press. (2006). Kreig, Elaine. "Helping Our Students." 14 June 1999, natl. ed.: R12.

    _____

4. What is the format for a *Chicago* style heading? _____

5. What type size is required by *Chicago* style? _____

6. What is the format for an in-text citation, in *Chicago* style? _____

7. How are titles of short works formatted? _____

8. How are titles of long works formatted? _____

9. You must cite when:

    _____

    _____

10. How are bibliography entries ordered, in *Chicago* style? _____

| **12-5b** | Using Chicago Style Format |

Directions: *Answer each question in a complete sentence.*

1. How are names formatted in citations, in *Chicago* style?

   _____

2. Where is the year of publication listed in a citation of a book, in *Chicago* style?

   _____

3. Besides the year of publication, what else is placed in parentheses for a book with one author?

   _____

4. Should papers written in *Chicago* style be double-spaced?

   _____

5. What is the preferred font and type size?

   _____

6. What is generally required in *Chicago*-style citations?

   _____

   _____

   _____

7. What information is required in a bibliography entry that cites a print book?

   _____

8. Write an example of journal citation?

   _____

9. Is the following cited correctly for a print article? If not, correctly cite.
   Mary Sledger, "The Rise and Fall," *Various Topics* 313 (2005); 121.

   _____

10. What is another name used to refer to *Chicago* style?

    _____

11. Do reference style lists use parenthetical citations?

    _____

12. Name a discipline that uses *Chicago* style.

    _____

12-5c | Using Chicago Style Format

Directions: *With a partner or group, write a citation for each of the specified source types on a separate sheet. Then, for each citation, scramble the order of information, and write the scrambled elements in the spaces provided below., Exchange worksheets with your partner or another group, and write the correct citations in Chicago format in the spaces indicated below. Discuss your responses.*

1. Website:

   _____

   _____

   _____

   _____

   _____

Citation: _____

2. Article from scholarly journal (online):

   _____

   _____

   _____

   _____

   _____

Citation: _____

3. Book with multiple authors:

   _____

   _____

   _____

   _____

   _____

Citation: _____

An Overview of the Writing Process

The stages of writing don't occur one right after the other. Typically, you will move among several of them every time you sit down to write. That's why the writing process is called "recursive"—you will go back to earlier stages even though the main task you are working on now is shown here as a later stage. For example, while you are revising a draft, you'll get some new ideas, which you'll explore by doing more prewriting.

Stage of Writing	Description	General Questions to Ask
Prewriting	• Think of ideas and issues to write about, using brainstorming, clustering, and asking the five W questions to spark thoughts and make connections. • *Brainstorming:* Make a list of possible topics. Select one or more that seem most interesting to you. Keep narrowing down your topic until it's the right size for the assignment. • *Clustering:* Draw a circle in the middle of a page and write a topic idea in it. Draw smaller circles around it to figure out how much you have to say about the topic. • *Five W's:* About any idea you may have at any stage, ask questions: Who, what, why, when, where, and how? Write down answers to each to figure out where your interest lies. • Jot down notes as you think. • Narrow down your ideas into a topic that works for this assignment.	• What exactly does the assignment ask me to do? • What is my general purpose for writing—am I supposed to inform readers, persuade them, tell them a story? • Who is my audience of readers? What do they know and believe? • What do I care about? • What am I interested in? • What problems should be discussed?
Outlining	• Organize your thoughts in terms of a hierarchy of ideas—larger ideas being supported by details of various kinds, such as facts, statistics, examples, quotes from experts, and so on. • Outlining can be done either before you write a draft, or afterward to check the flow of ideas, or even both. • Outlining doesn't mean your ideas are set in stone. Be flexible, and change your thesis, reasons, and details as needed as you write.	• What is the thesis statement that I will writing about? (It may keep changing throughout the writing process, and that's fine.) • What are the major reasons that support this thesis? • What are the supporting details that support each reason?

Drafting	• Write out your thinking in a rough form, understanding that you will almost certainly need to rewrite the whole thing. • Start by writing the body paragraphs, then circle back and write the introduction and conclusion. • Include all your ideas. Later, you can decide which ones are most important to keep.	• How are my various ideas connected to one another? • What am I really trying to say here? • How can I help this audience follow my thoughts and accept my ideas?
Peer Reviewing	• Get feedback on your draft	• Ask your classmate: • What is my thesis? • What are the strengths of my draft? • Where are ideas unclear? • What is one suggestion for improving this draft?
Incubating	• Pause for at least a few hours to allow your mind time to consider what you have learned from drafting and from any feedback you have received.	• Do not ask questions or think about your draft! Go for a walk; see a movie; visit a friend!
Revising	• Rewrite the whole paper, large sections, and paragraphs to address content and organizational issues	• How can I emphasize important ideas more? • How can I guide readers to follow my train of thought without getting lost? • What new ideas or details do I need to include? • Which ideas or details can I remove without weakening my paper? • How can I take my peer reviewer's comments into account while remaining true to my own vision?
Editing	• Rewrite sentences to ensure the best expression of ideas	• Are my sentences varied enough to keep readers interested? • Have I used sentence structure to make my ideas clear and memorable? • Have I used the best words to convey my meaning?
Proofreading	• Check spelling, punctuation, grammar, and citations for accuracy	• Have I punctuated sentences and words correctly? • Do subjects and verbs agree in number? • Are words all spelled correctly? • Have I included an in-text citation and a Works Cited (if MLA) or References (if APA) entry for each use of an outside source? • Is my paper formatted according to instructions?

MLA Style for Common Citations

The types of sources we use in research projects are always evolving, and the new *MLA Handbook* demonstrates an approach to simplify the task of citing them. Instead of asking writers to learn unique formats for each type of source, MIA style emphasizes citing traits shared across sources and formatting these traits in consistent ways. These are the nine core elements to consider when creating entries for your list of works cited; every source contains some combination—but not necessarily all—of them.

The Core Elements of a Works-Cited Entry

1. Author.	**Who created the source**—or whose work on the source you choose to emphasize first and foremost.
2. Title of source.	**The title of the *specific* source you are citing.** This could be a whole book or a short poem within it, if your focus is on that poem.
3. Title of container,	**The title of a larger source containing the source you are citing.** When a source stands alone (like a whole film or novel), there is no container. When an essay (source) is published in a journal (larger source), then that journal is called a *container.*
4. Other contributors,	**Noteworthy contributors to the work,** such as editors, translators, and performers.
5. Version,	**Description of a source that appears in more than one version,** such as a book in revised editions.
6. Number,	**Number indicating source's place in a sequence,** such as volume and issue numbers for journals, or season and episode numbers for television shows.
7. Publisher,	**Organization that produces or sponsors the source,** delivering it to readers.
8. Publication date,	**When the source was made available to the public.** This might be a year, a month, a specific date, or even a specific time.
9. Location.	**Where to find a specific source.** This could be page numbers for print sources; a URL or DOI for online sources; or the location of a lecture or performance.

The Elements of an In-Text Citation

Within the body of your paper, provide brief citations to any sources that you quote, paraphrase, or summarize. Each citation points readers to a more detailed entry in your list of works cited. The citation may be introduced with a signal phrase, contained in parentheses, or both.
parentheses, or both.

SIGNAL PHRASE	Critic Judith Thurman argues, "Ma Ke's couture dignifies the harshness of proletarian life" (54). *Note how a direct quotation is punctuated.*
NO SIGNAL PHRASE	In that political climate, attention to fashion was considered unpatriotic (Thurman 54). *Note how a paraphrase is punctuated.*

Long quotations. When citing a direct quotation that is four lines or longer, indent the quotation 1/2" from the margin. Do not use quotation marks, and place the period before the parenthetical citation, like so: …and peace is here. (319)

Formatting the Core Elements in a Works Cited Entry

1. Author	*Examples*
One author. Invert the author's name. For online sources, pseudonyms and handles may be used. Corporations can also be authors.	Jacob, Mira. King, Martin Luther, Jr. @PicadorUSA. Environmental Protection Agency.
Two authors. Invert the first author's name, but put the second name in traditional order. Separate them with a comma.	Pratchett, Terry, and Neil Gaiman.
Three or more authors. Name only the first author, followed by *et al.*	Raabe, William A., et al.
Beyond writers. The primary contributor could be an editor, a director, a composer, a performer, etc. Spell out roles after names.	Dunham, Lena, performer. Lamar, Kendrick, composer. Mayer, Richard E., editor.
2. Title of source	*Examples*
Longer works. For books, Web sites, films, and other standalone works, italicize them.	*Design for How People Learn*. *The Martian*.
Shorter works. For essays, poems, Web pages, and television episodes, place them in quotation marks.	"The Yellow Wallpaper." "The One with Phoebe's Wedding."
Sections of work (untitled).	Introduction. Afterword.
3. Title of container Italicize most containers.	*Examples*
When citing a standalone source, element 3 is not needed. When citing an essay *within* a book or an episode *of* a television show, the container is the book or show.	*The* New Yorker, *African American Review,* *Serial,* *The Unbreakable Kimmy Schmidt,*

4. *Other contributors,*	*Examples*
Introduce each name (or names) with a description of the role. If listed after element 2, capitalize the description; if listed after element 3, do not. If there are multiple roles you wish to emphasize, separate them with commas.	, translated by David McLoghlin, , adapted by Anne Carson, . Directed by Mira Nair, performance by Naseeruddin Shah.

5. *Version,*	*Examples*
Use abbreviations *ed.* (edition) and *rev.* (revised); spell out other words. Use numerals for numbered editions.	rev. ed., 3rd ed., updated ed., version 2.1,

6. *Number,*	*Examples*
Use abbreviations *vol.* (volume) and *no.* (issue), but spell out other descriptors, such as *episode.*	vol. 7, no. 11, season 1, episode 5,

7. *Publisher,*	*Examples*
List publishers for books, films, television shows, and sites that have sponsors that differ from their title and author. Separate multiple publishers with a slash (/).	Vintage Books, U of Virginia Library / Museum of Design,
Spell out most names, but omit initial articles and any corporate words (*Inc.*) Do use abbreviations for university presses (UP).	Melville House, Free Press, Rutgers UP, U of Michigan P,

NOTE: Do not list publishers for periodicals, sites for which titles and publishers are similar, or sites that do not produce the works they house. Do not include cities of publication.

8. *Publication date,*	*Examples*
This could mean the date a work was published, republished, released, broadcast, or performed.	2016, Jan-Feb. 2014, 10 May 2015, 9:30 p.m.,

NOTE: Access dates should only be included when a source is unstable or likely to change. Place these at the end of your citation, after the location.

9. Location	Examples
For sources with page numbers, use the prefix *p.* or *pp.*	p. 9. pp. 1065–89. pp. 185–89.
For sources accessed online, provide DOIs when given. If a DOI is not available, use a direct URL, ideally a permalink. Do not use angle brackets or any *http://* prefixes.	doi:10.1002/cplx.21590. milkdelivers.org/about-milkpep/. www.refinery29.com/fitness.

Containers within containers. Sometimes you will access sources in containers within larger containers. This means that if you cite an article from a journal (container #1) that you accessed through a database like EBSCOhost (container #2), then you should include relevant information about the larger container (such as its title and the source's location within it) to help readers retrace your steps. Place any information about container #2 after all information about the source itself and container #1, separated by a period.

See samples of how to cite sources like this in F, G, and I on the pages the follow.

Sample Works-Cited Entries: Books

A. Book.

PRINT

Oyeymi, Helen. *Mr. Fox: A Novel*. Riverhead Books, 2012.

ONLINE DATABASE   original pub. date (follows title)

Wells, H. G. *The Invisible Man: A Grotesque Romance*. 1897. *Bartleby.com*, 2000, bartleby. com/1003/.   date published online

E-READER (APP OR ON DEVICE)   translator

Cadhain, Máirtín Ó. *The Dirty Dust*. Translated by Alan Titley, Kindle ed., Yale UP, 2015.

B. Book with an author and an editor.

Woolf, Virginia. A *Writer's Diary*. Edited by Leonard Woolf, Harcourt, 1954.

C. Revised book

Chaucer, Geoffrey. *The Canterbury Tales: Fifteen Tales and the General Prologue*. Edited by V A. Kolve and Glending Olson, 2nd ed., W. W. Norton, 2005.

D. Selection from an anthology or textbook

Díaz, Junot. "Aurora." *The Ecco Anthology of Contemporary American Short Fiction*, edited by Joyce Carol Oates and Christopher R. Beha, Harper Perennial, 2008, pp. 213–26.

E. Book in a multivolume work

Kennedy, David M., and Lizabeth Cohen. *The American Pageant: Since 1865*, 15th ed., vol. 2, Wadsworth, 2012.

Sample Works-Cited Entries: Periodicals

F. Journal article

PRINT

Parikka, Jussi. "Earth Forces: Contemporary Land Arts, Technology, and New Materialist Aesthetics." *Cultural Studies* Review, vol. 21, no. 2, 2015, pp. 47–75.

ONLINE DATABASE

Pavlovic, R. Y. and A. M. Pavlovic. "Dostoevsky and   container #1

Psychoanalysis: Psychiatry in 19th-century Literature." *The British Journal of Psychiatry*, vol. 200, no. 3, 2012, p. 181. *EBSCOhost*, doi:10.1192/bjp.bp.111.093823.

       container #2

G. Magazine or newspaper article

PRINT

Brennan, William. "TV's Fake-Language Master." *The Atlantic*, April 2016, pp. 16–18.

Simon, Lizzie. "The Art of Obsession." *The Wall Street Journal*, 19 Mar. 2012, pp. A24+. A plus sign stands in for non-sequential pages.

ONLINE

Chen, Brian X. "Virtual Reality Is Here. Is Oculus Rift Worth It?" *The* New York Times, 28 Mar. 2016, nyti.ms/lXYcowB. permalink

ONLINE DATABASE

When there is no listed author, begin with title.

"Outsider Candidates Generating Buzz." *The Toronto Starr*, 19 Mar. 2016, p. A16. *LexisNexis Academic*, http://www.lexisnexis.com.proxy wexler.hunter.cunyedu/lnacui2api/api/versionl/getDocCui?l-ni=5JBB-WWG1-DY91-K4PR&csi=237924&hl=t&hv=t&hns-d=f&hns=t&hgn=t&oc=00240&perma=true.

Sample Works—Cited Entries: Other Source Types

H. Recording (music, film)

Beyoncé. "Flawless." *Beyoncé*, performance by Chimamanda Ngozi Adichie, Columbia Records, 12 Aug. 2014.

I. Episode or program (app, streaming service)

"Cops Redesign." *Portlandia*, directed by Jonathan Krisel, performances by Fred Armisen and Carrie Brownstein, season 2, episode 5, IFC, 3 Feb. 2012, *Netflix*, www.netflix.com/watch/70236274.

J. Podcast or video podcast (online)

Kine, Starlee, narrator. "Belt Buckle." *The Mystery Show*, episode 3, Gimlet, 18 June 2015, gimlet-media.com/episode/case-3-belt-buckle/.

K. Page on a Web site or blog post

Wise, Hannah. "An American Mystery: Who or What Is Killing All These Bald Eagles?" *The Scoop Blog, Dallas Morning News*, 28 Mar. 2016, 4:31 p.m., thescoopblog.dallasnews.com/2016/03/an-american-mystery-who-or-what-is-killing-bald-eagles.html/.

L. Map or chart

West Virginia State Map. Folded ed. Rand McNally, 2011.

M. Work of art
When referring to the work of art itself (not a reproduction of it in print or online), include the medium. Place the date of creation immediately after the title.

medium

da Vinci, Leonardo. Mona Lisa. 1517, oil on canvas. Louvre Museum, Paris.

medium
N. Advertisement

"Apple Watch - Dance." Advertisement. *YouTube*, 21 Oct. 2015, www.you-tube.com/user/Apple?v=fHE5WD0515Y.

O. Public speech or live performance

description of speech, which is untitled

Rankine, Claudia. Keynote Address. 2016 AWP Conference and Bookfair, 31 Mar. 2016, Los Angeles Convention Center.

location

P. Personal interview

interview subject

Sha-Mena Jackson. Personal Interview. 7 July 2015.

APA Style for Common Citations

In fields such as psychology, education, public health, and criminology, researchers follow the guidelines given in the *Publication Manual of the American Psychological Association*, Seventh Edition (APA, 2020) to document their work. Like MLA style, APA encourages brevity in documentation and uses in-text parenthetical citations of sources. At the end of an APA-style paper, the bibliography is called a references list.

If, after consulting the following, you have trouble formatting any specific kind of source, consult the APA manual or ask a librarian for assistance.

The Elements of an In-Text Citation

In APA style, in-text citations usually include a parenthetical component, but some or all relevant source information may be introduced in the sentence itself. Unlike MLA style, APA requires including the source's date in an in-text citation.

For summaries and paraphrases, include the author and date in parentheses; or if you introduce the author's name in the text, place only the date in parentheses.

ONE AUTHOR

Kane (2013) finds it problematic that participants were interviewed before, but not after, the experiment.

The results of a recent study suggest that people in homogeneous communities define "empathy" differently than people who live in heterogeneous communities (Perry, 2011).

TWO AUTHORS

Most cases of depression should be treated with therapy before introducing medication (Johnson & Olivier, 2010).

THREE OR MORE AUTHORS

After interviewing 1,000 subjects, Johnson et al. (2010) concluded that most Americans still attach certain stigmas to therapy.

When citing direct quotations, include the author, date, and page number(s) if the source uses them. You can organize this information in several ways.

OPTION #1

Built more than a decade before the Civil War, the North Branch Viaduct represents not only a feat of engineering but "a kind of time machine that provides a link between generations and centuries" (Richman, 2005, p. 33).

OPTION #2

In *The Bridges of New Jersey*, Richman (2005) claims that the North Branch Viaduct represents not only a feat of engineering but "a kind of time machine that provides a link between generations and centuries" (p. 33).

OPTION #3

"[The North Branch Viaduct] represents a kind of time machine that provides a link between generations and centuries" writes Richman (2005) in his study of New Jersey's bridges (p. 33).

Note: As demonstrated in Option #3, you can distinguish your own clarifying addition to a quotation by enclosing that addition in brackets.

A signal phrase or parenthetical citation for a quotation from a source with no page numbers, such as an online article, would include the author's name and date but no page numbers.

Formatting the Core Elements in a References Entry

Each of your in-text citations must lead readers to a more detailed entry listed on the "References" page at the end of your project.

1. Author	*Examples*
One author. Begin with the author's name when it is provided. Use initials for the author's first name (and middle name if given):	Kerman, P.
Two to 20 authors. Include all authors' names, last name first, initials afterward. Separate names with a comma. Before the final name, use an ampersand: &.	Brennan, L., Fein, D., Como, A., Rathwell, I., & Chen, C-M.
21 or more authors. Include the first 19 authors' names, using a comma after the initials of the 19th, add an ellipsis (three spaced dots), and then include the last named author. Do not use an ampersand before the final author's name.	Jaeger, E., Webb, E., Howarth, K., Carvajal-Carmona, L., Rowan, A., Broderick, P., Walther, A., Spain, S., Pittman, A., Kemp, Z., Sullivan, K., Heinimann, K., Lubbe, S., Domingo, E., Barclay, E., Martin, L., Gorman, M., Chandler, I. Vijayakrishnan, J., . . . Tomlinson, I.
Beyond the author. When referring to an edited book, put the editor's name in the author position and add in parentheses either (Ed.) for a single editor or (Eds.) for more than one. If referring to a chapter in an edited book, reverse the order of the chapter authors' first initials and last name but keep the regular order of the editors' names. Put the word In before the book editors' names.	Pelling, N. J., & Burton, L. J. (Eds). Palermo, M. T. & Greydanus, D. E. In J. Merrick (Ed.),
2. Publication Dates	*Examples*
Place the publication date in parentheses after the author's name. Some source types include a month and/or day in addition to the year.	(2010). (2018, June). (2017, March 1).

3. Titles	Examples
Placement and Formatting. The title of the work being cited comes after the publication date. Unlike in MLA style, shorter works (essay or article titles, songs, episodes) do *not* use quotation marks. Longer published works (books, periodicals, magazines, newspapers, websites, albums) are italicized.	Parental expectations and children's academic performance [article]
Capitalization. For books and all shorter works, capitalize only the first word of the title and of the subtitle and any proper nouns and proper adjectives. For the names of periodicals, however, capitalize all important words; these are treated as proper nouns.	*Journal of Sociology* [periodical] *Generation Z goes to college* [book]

4. Publication Information	Examples
Journals, newsletters, magazines. Put the volume number after the periodical title, in italics. If there is an issue number, put the issue number in parentheses after the volume number; do not italicize it. Provide the page numbers of the whole article.	*Monitor on Psychology, 49*(7), 24. *Journal of Youth and Adolescence, 40*, 479–489.
Books and reports. Give the publisher's name. If the author is also the same as the publisher, do not repeat the author's name.	Norton. University Press of Mississippi.

5. Additional Source Information	Examples
Other publication and access information varies among source types. For nonstandard types of sources, identify the type in brackets after the title and any parenthetical information.	[Letter to the editor]. [Audio podcast]. [Video].

6. Online Sources	Examples
When accessing a work (particularly a journal article) online or in a database, include its digital object identifier (DOI) if one is assigned.	https://doi.org//21.7894734911
If no DOI is assigned, use the source's URL. Do not place a period after the hyperlink.	https://climate.nasa.gov/causes/

Sample References Entries

A. Book

PRINT

Kerman, P. (2010). *Orange is the new black: My year in a women's prison*. Spiegel & Grau.

BOOK ACCESSED ONLINE

Gladwell, Malcolm. (2000). *The tipping point: How little things can make a difference.* Little, Brown and Company. https://www.littlebrown.com/titles/malcolum-gladwell/ the-tipping-point/97881600240089

B. Revised book

Insert information about the edition in parentheses, following the title but before the period.

Kendall, D. (2014). *Sociology in our times* (10th ed.). Cengage Learning.

C. Chapter in an edited book

Sacks, O. (2000). The last hippie. In J. Lethem (Ed.), *The Vintage book of amnesia: An anthology of writing on the subject of memory loss* (pp. 196–226). Vintage Books.

D. Entry in an encyclopedia or reference source

If no author is listed, begin with the entry title.

A guide to inventions and discoveries from Adrenaline to the Zipper. (2017, February 11). In *Infoplease.* https://www.infoplease.com/math-science/inventions-discoveries/ a-guide-to-inventions-and-discoveries-from-adrenaline-to-the-zipper

Sample References Entries: Periodicals

E. Journal article

PRINT

Furlong, M. J., & Christenson, S. L. (2003). Engaging students at school and with learning: A relevant construct for all students. *Psychology in the Schools, 45*(5), 365–368.

JOURNAL ACCESSED ONLINE

Furlong, M. J., & Christenson, S. L. (2008). Engaging students at school and with learning: A relevant construct for all students. *Psychology in the Schools, 45*(5), 365–368. https://doi.org/ l0.1002/pits.20302

ONLINE-ONLY JOURNAL

If volume, issue, or page numbers are available, include them in your entry.

Jamel, J. (2014). Do the print media provide a gender-biased representation of male rape victims? *Internet Journal of Criminology.* https://www.internetjournalofcriminology.com/Jamel_Print_Media _Representation_of_Male_Rape_Survivors_IJC_Jan_2014.pdf

F. Magazine article

PRINT

Matthews, J. T. (2014, August). Iraq illusions. *The New York Review of Books, 61*(13), 4.

ONLINE

Bouie, J. (2014, August 29). Keeping the police honest. *Slate*. https://slate.com/news-and
-politics/2014/08/policing-the-police-americans-law-enforcement-needs-greater
-accountability.html

G. Newspaper article

Do not include information about the edition or section.

PRINT

Kaplan, K. (2014, August 26). Lose weight to gain brain power? Study says it may work. *The Chi-cago Tribune*, 3:1.

ONLINE

MacVean, M. (2014, July 24). We're all in the clean-plate club, researchers conclude. *The Los Angeles Times*. https://www.latimes.com/science/sciencenow/la-sci-sn-clean-plate-club-20140724
-story.html

Sample References Entries: Other Source Types

H. Document or page from an online scholarly project or website

Include the author of the document or page (if listed); the date posted or updated in parentheses; the title of the page or document referenced (followed by the date if there is no author); the name of the larger site or project (italicized); and a hyperlink.

Bureau of Labor Statistics. (2020, February 20). The employment situation—January 2020.
U.S. Department of Labor. https://www.bls.gov/news.release/pdf/empsit.pdf

I. Blog

Patikar, M. (2014, August 31). Harness your mind's "future self" bias to make
better decisions. *Lifehacker*. http://lifehacker.com/harness-your-minds-future
-self-bias-to-make-better-de-1629209080

J. Comment on an article or post

Include the comment title or the first 20 words of the comment following the date.

KingKai90. (2014, September 1). I feel like my future self is Tyler Durden (albeit not extreme).
Although, I think are future selves ARE different [Comment on the blog post "Harness your mind's 'future self' bias to make better decisions"]. *Lifehacker*. http://lifehacker.com/
harness-your-minds-future-self-bias-to-make-better-de-1629209080/all

K. Lecture or speech

Italicize the title of the speech if there is one.

Springsteen, B. (2012, March). Keynote speech presented at South by Southwest Music Festival,
Austin, TX.

L. Film, Recording, Performance, Broadcast, or Podcast

List entries by the name of the most important contributor (director, producer, host, and so on). Identify the medium of access (Film, Video, Song, Audio podcast, TV episode) in brackets after the title. Include the name of the production company at the end of the citation.

Fincher, D. (Director). (2011). *The girl with the dragon tattoo* [Film]. Metro-Goldwyn-Mayer/ Columbia Pictures.

Lorde. (2012). Royals [Song]. On *Pure heroine*. Universal Music Group.